GREEN DESIGN

SUSTAINABLE BUILDING FOR IRELAND

Edited by Ann McNicholl and J. Owen Lewis
Energy Research Group, University College Dublin

OPW
Oifig na nOibreacha Poiblí
The Office of Public Works

Published by the Stationery Office

GREEN DESIGN : SUSTAINABLE BUILDING FOR IRELAND

1996 Baile Átha Cliath. Arna fhoilsiú ag Oifig an tSoláthair fé cheadúnas eisiach An Choláiste Ollscoile, Baile Átha Cliath.
1996 Dublin. Published by the Stationery Office under exclusive licence from University College Dublin.

ISBN 0-7076-2392-8
Publication No. EUR 16859 of the European Commission

Le ceannach díreach ón
Oifig Dhíolta Foilseachán Rialtais, Sráid Theach Laighean, Baile Átha Cliath 2.
To be purchased directly from
Government Publications Sales Office, Molesworth Street, Dublin 2.

nó/or

Ordú tríd an bPost ó Rannóg na bhFoilseachán, Oifig an tSoláthair, 4-5 Bóthair Fhearchair, Baile Átha Cliath 2.
(Teil: 01-661 3111, fó-líne 4040/4045; Facs: 01 475 2760)
By Mail Order from Publications Division, Government Supplies Agency, 4-5 Harcourt Road, Dublin 2.
(Tel: 01-661 3111, ext, 4040/4045; Fax: 01 475 2760)

nó trí aon díoltóir leabhar.
or from any bookseller

Available also from:
The Royal Institute of the Architects of Ireland, 8 Merrion Square, Dublin 2. Tel: 01 676 1703 Fax 01 661 0948
and
The Energy Research Group, School of Architecture, University College Dublin, Richview, Clonskeagh, Dublin 14. Tel. 01 269 2750 Fax 01 283 8908

PREPARATION

This book has been prepared within the ALTENER Project 'Training and Information for Architects in Passive Solar and Bioclimatic Design' , a task involving the Energy Research Group at University College Dublin, the Office of Public Works and the Royal Institute of the Architects of Ireland. The task was co-ordinated by the Energy Research Group, University College Dublin.

The Project is part-funded under the European Commission's ALTENER Programme, which supports training and information in renewable energies. The ALTENER Programme is an action of Directorate General XVII for Energy. In Ireland the ALTENER Programme is co-ordinated by the Department of Transport, Energy and Communications.

Design and principal photography : ARC Survey Photo Graphic Ltd, Dublin. ©
Printed by : The Turner Print Group, Longford and Dublin.

LEGAL NOTICE

FOREWORD

This book, a practical manual for sustainable design, has been prepared within the context of an ALTENER project, 'Training and Information for Architects in Passive Solar and Bioclimatic Design'. The ALTENER Programme, which in Ireland is co-ordinated by the Department of Transport, Energy and Communications, is an action of Directorate General XVII for Energy of the European Commission. Its objectives are to develop the use of renewable energy resources in the EU and to stabilise carbon dioxide emissions at their 1990 levels by the year 2000.

The project has been a joint undertaking of the Energy Research Group at University College Dublin, the Office of Public Works and the Royal Institute of the Architects of Ireland. This ALTENER project represents, for all three, a continuation of long-established policies.

For twenty-one years the Energy Research Group has been involved in research and dissemination on energy use in buildings and climate-sensitive architectural design. Most of these activities have had a strongly European dimension. This project presented a very welcome opportunity to develop materials designed specifically for the Irish context.

The Office of Public Works has traditionally promoted the appropriate use of indigenous materials and processes in the construction of its buildings. Its response to the Government's programme for reducing energy consumption has already resulted in major savings in many of the buildings under its care. The manual will be a useful tool in ensuring the continuation of these policies, while at the same time promoting the principle of sustainability within design.

One of the primary roles of the Royal Institute of the Architects of Ireland is to provide the information which its members need in order to discharge their responsibilities to their clients, and to the community as a whole. It is RIAI policy that sustainable design should be a significant component in the Continuing Professional Development of its members, and the results of this collaboration will be incorporated into its programme of seminars, workshops and practice supports.

'Green Design: Sustainable Building for Ireland' concentrates primarily on passive solar heating, natural cooling and daylighting. These are currently the most relevant renewable technologies for Irish buildings, but the potential of other forms of renewable energy is not ignored. Also included is guidance on the energy and pollution implications of building materials, on the protection of water resources and the reduction of waste.

While architects are the primary audience for the manual, the content should also be of use to services engineers, to students, and to interested members of the public. It is hoped that it will facilitate interdisciplinary discussion between the building professions during the early design stages, when most of the decisions which have major 'green' implications are taken.

ACKNOWLEDGEMENTS

PRINCIPAL CONTRIBUTORS

The following people prepared the material which forms the basis of the text

John Goulding, Energy Research Group, UCD.
Loughlin Kealy, School of Architecture, UCD.
David Kelly, Healy Kelly & Partners.
Paul Kenny, Energy Research Group, UCD.
Ciaran King, Energy Research Group, UCD.
Paul Leech, GAIA Associates.
John McCarthy, Coll McCarthy Architects.
Ann McNicholl, Energy Research Group, UCD.
Gioulli Mihalakakou, Energy Research Group, UCD.
Eoin O'Cofaigh, McHugh O'Cofaigh Architects.
Dermot O'Connell, School of Architecture, UCD.
John Olley, School of Architecture, UCD.

STEERING GROUP

The members of the Steering Group, who reviewed and advised on the direction taken by the work, were:

Mairead Broderick, Department of Transport, Energy and Communications
Loughlin Kealy, Chairman, Board of Architectural Education, RIAI
Paul Leech, Convenor, Committee on Sustainable Development, RIAI
J. Owen Lewis, Director, ERG, UCD, Co-ordinator
Larry McGettrick, Assistant Principal Engineer, OPW
Ann McNicholl, Research Architect, ERG
Klaus Unger, Assistant Principal Architect, OPW

REVIEW GROUP

The contribution of the following people, who assisted in the formulation of the brief for the book and in the review of draft material, is gratefully acknowleged.

Matt Barnes, Architect. David Keane, Keane Murphy Duff, and President, RIAI. Sean Mulcahy, VMRA Associates. Ciaran O'Connor, OPW. Gerard O'Sullivan, OPW. James O'Sullivan, OPW. Angela Rolfe, OPW. Des Thorpe, OPW. Martin Tritschler, Tritschler, Tritschler & Associates.

ASSISTANCE

The assistance of the following people, who contributed information and advice on a multiplicity of topics is also gratefully acknowledged.

Neil Crimmins, Energy Research Group, UCD. Dominique Dumortier, LASH-ENTPE, Lyon. Ken Beattie, DIT. William Burns, NSAI. Tony Cawley, Sanitary Services Dept., Dept. of the Environment. Nick Baker, Cambridge Architectural Research Ltd.. Kevin O'Rourke, Irish energy Centre. Eileen Fitzgerald, ERG, UCD. Patrick Minogue, Dept. of the Environment. Tom Walshe, Health and Safety Authority. Bill McComiskey, Environmental Protection Agency. Pierre Jolivet, ERG, UCD. Gus Cummins, Department of the Environment. Paul Littlefair, Building Research Establishment. Diarmuid de Búrca, Department of Agricultural and Food Engineering, UCD. Des McGrane, Paradigm Technology Ltd.. Maurice Costello and Ray Jennings, Pilkington Glass Ltd.. Olive Lynch, Buschbaum B.V.. B. Kümpers, Okalux Kappilarglas GmbH.. Fielden Clegg Architects. Frank Convery, Environmental Institute, UCD. Mike Buckley, BRECSU. Ray Noble, Ove Arup & Partners. Joanne Geary, Renewable Energy Information Office, Bandon. ENFO.. Ken Dodd, Hytherm (Irl) Ltd.. Vincent Dodd, Faculty of Engineering and Architecture, UCD. Bernard Gilna. Murray O' Laoire Associates. Andrew Wright, Richard Rogers Partnership. Alberto Campo Baeza. Teulades i Façanes Multifuncionals, S.A.. Sue Roaf, Oxford Brookes University. Pilkington Solar International. Architectenbureau Alberts & van Huut. Talos Engineering, S.A.. Roger Baumgarten, Renzo Piano Building Workshop. Jaime Lopez de Asiain. Poul Kristensen, Esbensen. Consulting Engineers. Marco Sala, Dept. of Architectural Technology, University of Florence. Ales Krainer, Faculty of Civil Engineering and Geodesy, University of Lubljana. Dag Roalkvam, GAIA Lista. Lars Højensgårds Tegnestue. Helmut Ziehe, International Institute for Bau-Biologie and Ecology, Inc.. Andrew Ogorzalek, PCKO Architects. K. Buntkiel-Luck, Siemens. Herzog & Partner. John Talbott, Findhorn Foundation. Bosco Büeler, ECOHB Global Network of Organisations for Environmentally-Conscious and Healthy Building. Simos Yannas, Architectural Association School of Architecture. Eugene McLernan, Scott Tallon Walker. Tom Coughlan, Burke-Kennedy Doyle & Partners. Colin Hudson, Pittsburgh Corning, UK.

CONTENTS

INTRODUCTION

In *The Architecture of the Well-Tempered Environment*, Reyner Banham described the revolution in architectural form and expression which followed the introduction of mechanical services. The invention of electric lighting, central heating, lifts and air conditioning transformed people's expectations of buildings and expanded the range of what was architecturally possible. There is the potential for another shift, just as radical in kind, in the development of an architecture for the sustainable environment

Writing in 1969, Banham saw the possibility of buildings which were all fabric, without any additional power at all. In the final chapter of his book he reviewed St. George's County Secondary School in Wallasey, completed in 1961, which combined massive structure and a south-facing double-skin glazed wall to exploit "the oldest and ultimate source of all environmental power, the sun". This, he said, performed well because its designer took a total view of the complete man-structure-lighting-ventilating system. (Banham, 1969) In sustainable design we extend that system outwards to take in the neighbourhood and the globe.

> *"The concept of sustainability . . . requires that development must be within the capacity of the environment to support it without suffering lasting damage or depletion;"* *(Moving Towards Sustainability, Department of the Environment, May 1995)*

Applying this principle to the construction and use of buildings presents a challenging agenda to the building design professions, and to the construction industry as a whole.

Irish Life, Dublin, A & D Wejchert

Most building designers are now aware, in a general way, of actions which they can take to reduce damage to the environment and to the people who use buildings. During the briefing stage of this 'Green Design' project it became apparent that many were already committed to making use of renewable energies and to reducing the environmental impact of new construction. What they needed were the tools and information which would assist them in following 'green' or sustainable principles throughout a design and construction process constrained by intense pressures on time and finance.

This publication attempts to meet these needs by setting out the principles of sustainable design, combined with technical material and design guidance specific to Ireland's climate and construction practices. The context within which Irish building professionals operate, the roles played by others in the building procurement process, and the current state of renewable energies in Ireland are taken into account.

The focus is on architectural strategies, but there is also advice on the effective integration of conventional systems for heating, lighting and ventilation. Guidelines for the selection of materials and for the reduction of waste are included.

The objective was to produce a practical manual, to be used and referred to during the design process. Each section sets out underlying principles and lists the strategies that might be adopted for that aspect of building performance. Sources of more detailed and more extensive information - people, organisations or publications - are provided in almost every section. For many projects the manual may be sufficient in itself; in other circumstances the design team will be wise to seek expert advice. For the practitioner who wants to develop more expertise in sustainable design, the manual should provide a starting point.

ARCHITECTURE & SUSTAINABILITY

Rockfleet Castle, Clew Bay, Co. Mayo

Architecture has always involved the creative use of natural resources to serve human purposes. There is also a long and inventive tradition in the making of buildings that are sensitive to place and to climate. In the late twentieth century these two concepts have taken on added meaning. We all know now that our world is more fragile than we had imagined, and that the cumulative effect of small decisions can unsettle its precarious ecological balance. Buildings play a surprisingly large role in that balance, and the design decisions taken by architects and engineers have calculable impact.

The effect of a building on the global environment is only one part of an increasingly complex equation. Its effects on the health and comfort of occupants, neighbours, and the workers who have to construct it are also part of the picture, one that is increasingly the subject of legislation. The objective, which is demanding but achievable, is to design buildings that are environmentally friendly at both the global and the local scale.

'Green Design', 'Energy-Conscious Design', 'Passive Solar Design', 'Bioclimatic Architecture', 'Ecological Design' and 'Sustainable Architecture'; we have seen all of these terms used in recent years. Their meanings overlap and some have been around for longer than others, but, of all of them, 'Sustainable Architecture' is the most recent and the most all-encompassing. The UIA (International Union of Architects) Declaration of Interdependence for a Sustainable Future, Chicago, 1993, proclaims:

> "Sustainable design integrates consideration of resource and energy efficiency, healthy buildings and materials, ecologically and socially sensitive land-use, and an aesthetic sensitivity that inspires, affirms, and ennobles." (Appendix 1)

The basic principles of sustainable design are quite straightforward: minimise artificial lighting, heating and mechanical ventilation; avoid air-conditioning; conserve water; use site and materials wisely; recycle where possible. A great deal can be achieved by intelligent design and without using untried technologies. The role of installed services is refined and the role of form and fabric expands. A new design vocabulary emerges, no longer dominated by awkward solar panels and incongruous conservatories. Sustainable architecture can provide buildings which are more economic, more comfortable, more humane, and more beautiful.

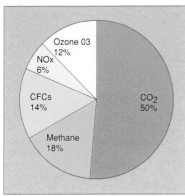

Contribution of greenhouse gasses to global warming

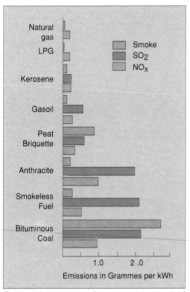

Pollution from domestic fuels: typical emissions of smoke, sulphur dioxide, and oxides of nitrogen per unit energy content. Source: EOLAS.

I   BUILDINGS AND THE BIOSPHERE

Buildings make a large contribution to the pollution of our air, our water and our physical environment. Constructing buildings makes considerable demands on natural resources; using them makes more. It follows that good sustainable design decisions taken by architects and engineers will have real benefits.

Buildings generate 'greenhouse gasses' which contribute to global warming. Carbon dioxide (CO_2) emissions contribute fifty per cent of the 'greenhouse effect' and in Western Europe half of those emissions are produced by heating, lighting and cooling buildings. (In Ireland, housing alone produces more CO_2 than either the transport or industrial sectors.) Generating electricity to manufacture building materials and construct buildings produces yet more carbon dioxide. Deforestation, in which the production of timber for the building industry plays some part, reduces the earth's capacity to convert that carbon dioxide into oxygen.

The quantity of CFCs (chlorofluorocarbons) in the atmosphere is relatively small, but weight for weight they are ten to twenty thousand times more damaging than carbon dioxide. In addition to depleting the ozone layer, CFCs are responsible for about fifteen per cent of the greenhouse effect. In Western Europe ten per cent of CFC use is related to refrigerants, insulation and solvents used in buildings.

Electricity consumed by building services accounts for a significant proportion of sulphur dioxide (SO_2) and nitrous oxide (NO_x) emissions. Dissolved to form acid rain, these chemicals are killing forests, threatening animal life and damaging buildings across Europe. At the local level SO_2, NO_x, and CO_2 in the air cause health problems, particularly to vulnerable members of the population; children, pregnant women, the elderly, and people with respiratory problems.

The European Union has set itself the target of stabilising CO_2 emissions at 1990 levels by the year 2000. Use of CFCs is to be phased out by 1997. If these targets are to be met, changes in the way we design, construct and service buildings are unavoidable.

The emergence of a philosophy of sustainable architecture is a response not only to this global dilemma, but also to the economic, social and cultural consequences of untrammelled expansion - the destruction of agricultural land, wildlife habitats, archaeological and architectural treasures, and living communities.

2   SUSTAINABLE ARCHITECTURE

Traditional building practices were intelligent responses to familiar circumstances. People took for granted the need to site buildings so as to maximise shelter, or to create it through planting. They made sure that the movement of water was controlled. Ground water was diverted through stone drains, and the penetration of rainwater was resisted by materials that allowed the building to breathe. The arrangement of spaces and the placing of openings reflected awareness of daily and seasonal cycles. From the scale of the landscape down to the construction details, simple vernacular buildings and formally composed works of architecture demonstrated intelligent decision-making. This sophistication arose from an appreciation of the need to work with, rather than against, the characteristics of site and climate, and from a thorough understanding of techniques and materials whose performance had been observed and modified over long periods of time.

From our perspective today, we can see that thoughtfulness about site, climate and materials persisted in the work of many of the masters of the Modern Movement, though the focus of critical attention lay elsewhere. It is clearly visible in what became known as 'Organic Architecture' ; in the work of architects such as Henry van de Velde and

Frederich Mendelson, in the section of Wright's prairie houses, or in Aalto's manipulation of space and materials. Kenneth Frampton has described the later work of Le Corbusier as "the monumentalisation of the vernacular", reflecting Le Corbusier's abiding concern with the sun, site and climate, and the transformation of his architecture as his interest in materials expanded (Frampton, 1985). Paolo Soleri exploited the capacity of form and materials to modify the climate of the Arizona desert, and the architecture of Hassan Fathy is a celebration of traditional Arab vernacular within a modern context.

Sustainable principles now underlie much of the work of practices as diverse as Sir Norman Foster & Partners, Fielden Clegg Design, Jourda & Perraudin Architects, Boje Lundgard, Alberto Campo Baeza, Architektburo Herzog or Michael Hopkins & Partners. As we can see from these examples, the sustainable character of a building can be made visually explicit, or be completely hidden. There is nothing stylistically prescriptive about sustainable design.

The context within which we build is complex and fast changing. Although sustainable architecture is part of a continuing tradition, we cannot rely on an uncritical return to the forms and technologies of the past. The informed design response to site and climate, and the willingness to exploit environment-friendly materials and technologies, must meet today's demands.

3   THE IMPLICATIONS FOR PRACTICE

Clients increasingly expect some consideration of green issues to be part of the standard service offered by the design team. Public sentiment, EU and national legislation, and the commercial property market, are increasingly demanding 'environment-friendly' buildings. Running costs, energy labelling and Sick Building Syndrome are in the minds of the people who rent or purchase property. Developers and investors, looking at profits and long-term rental performance, are taking notice. A 1991 guide for property owners and developers published in London advised:

> "The design and construction team should have up-to-date knowledge and experience related to minimising energy consumption and carbon dioxide emissions, have a strategy for the selection of environmentally acceptable building materials, have an awareness of how to minimise the possible factors leading to complaints such as Sick Building Syndrome and finally, know how to ensure that an effective and acceptable maintenance management system is set up at hand-over, particularly in air-conditioned buildings." (Jones Lang Wooton, 1991)

This presents the design team with extra responsibilities, but also with opportunities. In many respects sustainable design draws on the existing skills of the team and taking on the challenge is simply a matter of awareness and intention. Becoming and remaining informed about environmental issues in building at a basic level should by now be a routine part of keeping a practice up-to-date.

However, sustainable design is a fast-changing field, so established procedures and guidelines are thin on the ground. Getting access to reliable information and evaluating conflicting advice are just two of the problems a practice is faced with. The implementation of green design within a practice will almost certainly involve extra design time, particularly if the practice is new to it. If the project is to have a radically green agenda, the extra design time will be substantial, even for the most expert 'green' practice.

Collaboration between all the members of the design time during the early stages of a project is always beneficial. For sustainable design it is essential. Current fee structures for services engineers, which are based on a percentage of the services construction costs, are not helpful. An engineer who invests extra design time in working with the architect to reduce the financial and energy costs of artificial heating, lighting and ventilation will be penalised by receiving a lower fee.

New responsive bioclimatic shelter to bronze age city, Akrotiri, Santorini, N. Fintikakis architect.

Effective Management

Environmental Issues | Business Issues

Energy
Waste
Materials
Ecology and
Landscape
Transport
Internal
Environment

Commercial
and
Environmental
success

Finance
Function
Health
Delight
Cost in use
Productivity
Legislation
Marketing
Peer pressure
Stakeholders

Professional Responsibility
Duty of Care

Environmental and business issues affecting building and civil engineering projects. Source: Clients Guide, CIRIA, 1995

NMB Bank, Amsterdam, Architectenbureau Alberts & Van Huut.

4 THE CLIENT

The client's role is critical. In some circumstances he or she has no choice; an Environmental Impact Assessment is required by law, or health and safety legislation precludes the use of specific materials. But, if the design is to push beyond the minimum levels of performance required by current legislation, design and construction costs may rise, familiar and dependable service systems may be curtailed, and the burden of building management may increase. Why should a client take this on? Lower running costs, avoidance of Sick Building Syndrome and lower rates of absenteeism are incentives. So is productivity. Recent US studies have shown that making a building environmentally responsive can increase productivity by from six to fifteen per cent (Browning and Romm, 1995). Since most employers spend considerably more on salaries than they do on energy, this represents an even more attractive benefit than the savings on their fuel bills.

A building that looks and feels good to work in will support any company's quality assurance programme and contribute to its public image. Recent advertising campaigns by companies like The Body Shop demonstrate that a 'green' company image is seen as a market advantage. The experience of NMB in the Netherlands bears this out. The bank considers that its highly publicised, eighty-five thousand square metre, eco-friendly headquarters, which uses only one tenth the energy per square metre consumed by its former HQ, has been a factor in its advance to the position of second largest banking company in the country.

5 DESIGN TEAM POLICY

The building professions have always held that they have, in addition to their obligations to the client, a responsibility to the community. Attention to the impact of a building on the global and the local environment is simply an extension of this responsibility. At the UIA World Congress in Chicago in 1993 the architectural profession made the commitment to "place environmental and social sustainability at the core of our practices and professional responsibilities."

This is an ambitious objective, but practitioners already have most of the skills required. The critical issues are awareness, design time, and information.

FURTHER READING

- Barnett, Dianna Lopez and William D. Browning. *A Primer on Sustainable Building.* Snomass, Colo., Rocky Mountain Institute, 1995. $16.95. Fax +1 970 927-4178. Covers all of the issues and arguments in a very readable style aimed at professionals and interested laypersons.

- Construction Industry Research and Information Association (CIRIA). *A Client's Guide to Greener Construction.*(SP 120). London, CIRIA, 1995. £15.00. Fax +44 171 222 1708. Covers the environmental and economic benefits of sustainable practice in building and civil engineering projects.

- *Going Green. The Green Construction Handbook: A Manual for Clients and Construction Professionals.* Research by Ove Arup & Partners. Bristol, JT Design Build Ltd., 1993. Fax +44 1272 290946. Covers the fundamental concepts of 'green' building and provides one-page summaries on generic systems and materials.

- Jones Lang Wooton, McKenna & Co, and Gardiner & Theobald. *A New Balance: Buildings and the Environment: a Guide for Property Owners and Developers.* London, 1991. Jones Lang Wooton Fax +44 171 493 9539. 58 pp.

- *RIAI Policy on Sustainable Development.* Dublin, Royal Institute of the Architects of Ireland, [to be published in 1996].

SUSTAINABLE ARCHITECTURE IN AN IRISH CONTEXT

Irish Energy Centre, Dublin, Energy Research Group

Sustainable architecture is not designed in a vacuum. Ireland's physical climate, its planning and building regulations, the standards of comfort people expect, and the state of renewable energy technologies in this country all help determine what sustainable design strategies are appropriate or feasible. These four issues are examined in detail elsewhere in the manual, but there are other factors which have an impact on sustainability.

Of all of the people involved in the construction and management of buildings, the members of the design team have the single greatest influence on the degree to which a building will be environment-friendly. But other groups - clients, occupiers, investors, legislators, public authorities, utility companies, product manufacturers and building contractors - may help or hinder the production of sustainable architecture.

I PUBLIC POLICY

Many of the factors which contribute to a building's impact on the environment lie entirely outside the design team's control. Fuel pricing policies, local authority development plans, public transportation systems and waste disposal services, for example, are all significant, and policies in these areas often encourage the wasteful use of resources. The pricing policies of An Bord Gáis, which set minimum consumption levels and minimum annual payments for customers availing of economy tariffs, are a case in point. The promotion by the Electricity Supply Board of electric space heating is another.

At the level of urban design, Local Development Plans requiring minimum garden sizes make population densities greater than 160 persons per hectare unachievable in practice. At these densities the provision of good public transport, and of commercial and social facilities within walking distance, becomes uneconomic, so that dependence on private car use is increased.

Multiple use of facilities, which exploits the financial and environmental investment in existing buildings, and reduces the need for new ones, is often frustrated by lack of co-operation between public, community and commercial organisations

2 THE PROPERTY MARKET

A sustainably designed building which provides humane and comfortable conditions at low running costs should be highly rentable and have increased market value. However, uncertainty about market response to non-conventional solutions encourages a conservative stance among some letting agents and funding institutions. General lack of awareness of operating costs results in many decisions being taken largely on the basis of capital costs. Many of the advantages of a green building accrue to the tenant, rather than to the owner, and the fact that achieving lower running costs sometimes involves higher construction costs than are usual in speculative developments does not offer much encouragement to developers. Certification schemes, such as NICER or BREEAM, which provide energy efficiency or environmental ratings for buildings, may make it financially more rewarding to have a 'green' building to put on the market.

3 THE CONSTRUCTION INDUSTRY

Risk avoidance is not confined to clients and investors. Lack of experience, issues of liability, and the absence of agreed standards discourage design professionals, building contractors and building product manufacturers from moving away from tried and tested ways of doing things.

The design team can only build with the materials available. Ireland still retains to some extent a craft-based building industry using sustainable materials, and this is a resource which should not be underestimated. Its tradition in rendering is one example However, the difficulties of the building products sector have to be recognised. There is heavy investment in established working methods on which many livelihoods depend. This cannot be changed overnight. Opportunities for change arise when existing plant becomes obsolete, and 'tooling up' can be planned to maximum advantage if manufacturers are made aware of changing demand and specification practices well in advance. Properly handled, the move towards sustainable products offers manufacturers opportunities for diversification, competitive advantage and greater market share.

4   STANDARDS AND LABELLING

Even the most enlightened or adventurous manufacturer will hesitate to bring to the market new product types for which there are no national or international standards, no agreed test criteria. If they do, designers are reluctant to specify them and contractors to use them.

Since the early 1980s design professionals, building contractors and construction product manufacturers have been calling for a unified approach to the certification and labelling of sustainable materials. For example, designers and contractors find it almost impossible at present to truly establish the source of timber when it arrives on site. Materials described as "CFC free" in the sales brochure may contain alternatives which are equally harmful. Progress has been slow and proposals are currently being hotly contested at European level. Introducing a protocol which meets international standards, which combines scientific rigour with usefulness to specifiers and fairness to producers, will demand a concerted effort by Irish agencies working with the international bodies.

5   MAKING PROGRESS

There is growing awareness in the property market and among the general public. There is a discernible trend towards more daylighting and away from air-conditioning. Somewhat more sustainable building products are appearing on the market. And we have the 1995 Waste Bill, and the proposed revisions to Part L of the Building Regulations. These are all signs of progress in the right direction.

The Department of the Environment's publication, *Moving Towards Sustainability*, notes that one of the principles on which environmental policy in Ireland is based is "the principle of shared responsibility for the environment which requires a broadly based involvement of public bodies, private enterprise and the general public so as to achieve environmental policy objectives". Focused and thoughtful application of this principle is needed if we are to overcome the many outstanding difficulties.

RENEWABLE
ENERGIES

Renewable energies contribute about 2.3 percent of primary energy demand in Ireland. This is half the EU average. (The contribution of passive solar energy is not included in this figure. It reduces demand rather than generating alternative supply and is difficult to quantify.) At present only hydro-power and biomass are exploited commercially. The potential for renewables is far greater, but cheap fuel imports, abundant peat resources and over-capacity in electricity generation plant have discouraged development. The Alternative Energy Requirement (AER) scheme, launched in 1994, is intended to encourage private developers to undertake renewable energy projects which would generate electricity and supply it to the ESB. The scheme covers hydro, wind, solar, landfill gas, waste and biomass.

From the design team's point of view market potential is not the issue. The renewable energies of interest are those which can be incorporated in a building project and provide good environmental conditions with acceptable payback. However, the use of conventional commercial criteria and time scales in assessing returns on investment produces distorted results. The three-year payback period often used in calculating returns is not a suitable criterion for investment in sustainability. Ten years would be more appropriate. What is more, cost-effectiveness is usually calculated in relation to current fuel prices, which discount or omit the 'external costs' - such as environmental pollution, waste disposal and plant decommissioning - associated with most conventional energy sources. If the EU moves to redress this imbalance through taxation policies which penalise polluting fuels, the renewable energies will become a more attractive option in simple financial terms.

Renewable energies are not entirely trouble free. A wind farm or waste-burning plant does have environmental impacts. However, on balance, the environmental trade-off is better than for conventional fuels.

1 PASSIVE SOLAR

The renewable with by far the greatest potential to meet energy needs in Irish buildings is passive solar energy. Our temperate climate and surprisingly high level of solar radiation mean that a substantial percentage of the fossil-fuel based energy currently consumed by building services could be displaced. The 'technology' in the case of passive solar energy is the architecture of the building itself. Because of its potential, and because it is the area in which an architect can make the greatest contribution, this manual will concentrate primarily on techniques for the exploitation of passive solar energy.

The possibilities of other sources of renewable energy are described below. Some operate only at scales much larger than that of a single building project, but others are becoming increasingly viable at the small scale, particularly when used in tandem with passive solar strategies. Wind power, hydro power and photovoltaics in particular have advanced in reliability and sophistication in the last decade.

2 ACTIVE SOLAR

Active solar water heating systems can deliver 80 to 90 percent of domestic hot water requirements during the summer months, 15 to 20 percent in winter, with an annual average of about 50 percent. The technology has developed significantly in recent years, and installed costs of a system for a 4-person household are currently in the range £2000 to £4000. Larger, non-domestic installations have lower cost per square metre of collector area, and can provide pay-back periods which are acceptable in conventional accounting terms.

The Green Building, Dublin, Murray O'Laoire.
Roofspace including wind generators and PV panels.

Active solar space heating can make a contribution in some circumstances. Current developments include a space and water heating package, aimed at the Irish speculative housing market, in which the solar collectors form an integral part of structural and weatherproof roof units, and both heating and ventilation are provided by an air handling system which incorporates heat recovery. In principle, similar systems could be used in larger, non-domestic applications. Accommodation of fairly large areas of south-facing solar collector would be a critical factor. Contact: *Pat Walshe, Cork County Council Energy Agency Office, Spa House, Mallow, Co. Cork Tel (022) 43610 Fax (022) 43678 or Dr. Sean McCarthy, Hyperion, Main Street, Watergrasshill, Co. Cork. Tel (021) 889461 Fax (021) 889 465*

3 HYDRO

For the small number of buildings located close to a river or stream with adequate head and flow, hydro-power is worth considering. The technology is very well developed and further advances are making the exploitation of sites with low head or low flow-rates economic. In recent years many new installations have been commissioned and existing ones refurbished. *Contact: Irish Hydro Power Association, 13 Marlborough Road, Donnybrook, Dublin 4. Tel (01) 668 0043 Fax (01) 668 0043*

4   WIND

Ireland has one of the best wind resources in Europe, and 'wind farms' are likely to provide an increasing percentage of Ireland's electricity demand during the next decade. A typical wind farm might consist of ten 500 kW turbines with a total generating capacity of 5 MW. On a windy site the annual power production would be equivalent to the yearly electricity consumption of 3,000 houses. The cost of the power would be comparable to that for a new coal-fired power station. The privately owned wind farm at Bellacorrick power station in Co. Mayo may gradually replace peat-burning, while taking advantage of the high capacity power line already existing on the site.

Small turbines are proportionately more expensive and technically less well developed than larger commercial ones, and the installed cost of a domestic 2 - 6 kW turbine at present is relatively high. Nevertheless, turbines of this size could be used to provide power for isolated rural houses, particularly in coastal or upland areas. Very small turbines for lighting and other small loads are already economic, and can provide valuable back-up in areas where supply from the grid is unreliable. But if the primary objective is to reduce fossil fuel consumption, then insulation and other conventional measures have greater priority.

For projects with large electricity demand, and located close to suitable wind-resource sites, installation of one or two 150 kW or larger turbines may be justified. Installed costs for a typical commercial 500 kW turbine, whose annual power production would be equivalent to the yearly electricity consumption of 300 houses, are about £800 - £1000 per kW (in 1995), and falling. It is hoped that a new wind-energy scheme to be announced by the Department of Energy may make provision for installations at this scale to sell any surplus power to the ESB. The price paid by the ESB for this electricity would be a critical issue. *Contact: Irish Wind Energy Association, Arigna, Carrick-on-Shannon, Co. Roscommon. Tel (078) 46229 Fax (078) 46016.*

5   PHOTOVOLTAICS

Generating electricity using photovoltaic (solar) cells is effective even in cloudy weather and at low to moderate air temperatures. Photovoltaic systems have no moving parts, are noiseless, and produce no emissions in operation. Because they are built up in modules, there are no limits, other than available space, to the size of the installation. They are most suited to buildings where the electricity demand corresponds to daylight hours. It is estimated that for the South of England a 2.5 kW array of high efficiency modules, occupying 16m^2 of roof space, would produce an average output of about 6.5 kWh per day in July and about 2 kWh per day in January (Treble, 1993). New developments include photovoltaic roof tiles and photovoltaic cladding panels which form part of the building envelope, avoiding the costs associated with additional supporting structures and the conventional building materials which would otherwise be used.

The photovoltaic system can be linked to the ESB distribution network through an inverter. When the sun shines the PV installation provides the building with electricity and feeds any surplus into the network; when it does not shine power is supplied by the ESB. Buildings which are not connected to the ESB grid can use batteries to store PV generated electricity. Appliances using a 12 or 24 volt d.c. supply can operate directly off the batteries; appliances which use a 230 volt ac. mains supply will need an inverter.

The cost of photovoltaic cells is falling rapidly. It is estimated that within five years mass production will halve present costs. PV is already cost-effective in certain off-grid installations. *Contact: Dr. Sean McCarthy, Hyperion, Main Street, Watergrasshill, Co. Cork. Tel (021) 889461 Fax (01) 889 465*

Siemens, Solar Wechselstram System 600. A PV package which can provide power for domestic TV, refrigerators and lighting.

6   WASTE AND BIOMASS

Burning biogas from animal wastes to provide heat or power may be an option in some locations. Biomass crops or solid wastes (sawmill by-products and certain types of municipal waste, for example) can be burnt, gasified or digested to provide heat. If new timber is to be used as a fuel it should come from sustainably managed forests. The amount of carbon dioxide released in these processes is equal to that which would be released if they were allowed to decay naturally, so they can be considered CO_2 neutral. But the scale of operation is critical. It must be large enough to pay for the flue-gas cleaning equipment and controls which ensure efficient processing and prevent the release of other pollutants into the atmosphere.

A single-family house located on a wooded site can be self-sufficient, on a sustainable basis, if a very high-efficiency, low-emission stove or boiler is specified. *For biomass, contact: Teagasc, 19 Sandymount Ave., Dublin 4. Tel (01) 668 8188 Fax (01) 668 8023. For waste, contact: Dr. Gerard Kiely, Integrated Waste Management Group, Department of Civil and Environmental Engineering, University College Cork.. Tel (021) 2765648 Fax (021) 902965.*

Biomass crops, such as short rotation forestry, can be used to generate energy.

7   LANDFILL GAS

The decay of municipal waste at landfill sites produces combustible gases, such as methane, which are normally released to the atmosphere. These gasses can be collected and burned to produce electricity and or heat. A number of such schemes are in operation in other countries, and contracts for five schemes were offered by the Government in March 1995. This is not likely to be relevant at the scale of an architectural project. *Contact: Dr. Gerard Kiely, Integrated Waste Management Group, Department of Civil and Environmental Engineering, University College Cork.. Tel (021) 2765648 Fax (021) 902965.*

8   WAVE AND TIDAL

Ireland has a very large potential wave energy resource, but the technology is still at the research stage. Over 1000 patents for wave power devices exist world-wide and a number of prototypes have been built, but wave energy is not expected to become commercially viable for some time. In the long term, open sea devices have good potential for large-scale power generation. Small-scale turbines (100 - 150 kW) have been built and are at the demonstration stage. There are few problems with the turbines themselves, but the costs of the engineering works necessary to keep them in place under storm conditions make them un-competitive.

Tidal power conversion is most practical at locations where there is a large difference between high and low tide levels, and a tidal barrier at La Rance, France, has operated reliably since the mid-1960s. Long narrow estuaries tend to be most suitable, but the very high capital cost and severe environmental impact are obstacles to development. *Contact: Dr. Tony Lewis, Director, Hydraulics and Maritime Research Centre, Munster Institute, University College Cork. Tel (021) 902165 Fax (021) 343580.*

9   DESIGN TEAM POLICY

As is evident, not all of the renewable energy technologies have reached technical and commercial maturity. Before proceeding with any proposal, the design team should confirm at an early stage that the necessary hardware can be sourced within reasonable cost and time limits, and that backup, in terms of servicing, parts and technical advice, will be available to the client on a continuing basis.

GENERAL CONTACTS

- Renewable Energy Information Office, Irish Energy Centre, c/o South Western Services Coop, Shinagh House, Bandon, Co. Cork. Tel (023) 42193 Fax (023) 41304.
- ENFO, The Environmental Information Service, 17 St. Andrew St., Dublin 2. Tel (01) 679 3144 Fax (01) 679 5204
- Earthwatch (Friends of the Earth Ireland), Harbour view, Bantry, Co. Cork. Tel (027) 50968 Fax (027) 50545.
- Greenpeace Ireland, 44 Upper Mount St., Dublin 2. Tel (01) 661 9836 Fax (01) 660 5258.

FURTHER READING

- Energie-Anlagen Berlin. *Photovoltaic Technologies and their Future Potential.* Berlin, EAB - OPET for the European Commission, 1993. 29 pp. Free. Available from: Energy Research Group, School of Architecture, University College Dublin, Richview, Clonskeagh, Dublin 14. Tel (01) 269 2750 Fax (01) 283 8908

- Gonzálvez, C. H. and others. *Basic Aspects for Application of Wind Energy.* Madrid, IDAE - OPET for the European Commission, 1994. 25 pp. Free. Available from: Energy Research Group, School of Architecture, University College Dublin, Richview, Clonskeagh, Dublin 14. Tel (01) 269 2750 Fax (01) 283 8908

- Treble, Frederick C. *Solar Electricity: a Layman's Guide to the Generation of Electricity by the Direct Conversion of Solar Energy.* Birmingham, Solar Energy Society, 1993. Tel +44 121 459 1248 Fax +44 121 459 8206. 36 pp. Includes guidance on system sizing.

DESIGN STRATEGIES FOR SUSTAINABLE ARCHITECTURE

APPROACHING A SUSTAINABLE DESIGN PROJECT

Agreeing sustainable objectives with the client and the rest of the design team at the outset is a necessary first step. Clarity of purpose is essential in circumstances where some or all of the participants may be new to sustainable design, and new ways of thinking and working are demanded of them.

Everyone involved needs to visualise the building not as an autonomous object, but as one element within a system which should be disrupted as little as possible. We have to think in terms of the entire life cycle of the building and of the materials of which it is made; from extraction or harvesting of the raw materials, through the manufacturing process, transport, construction, use, maintenance, renewal, re-use and decay to, finally, recycling or disposal.

Getting the concept right is fundamental. Once outline proposals have been finalised, most of the critical decisions will have been made. The moves that are made in the very first stages of the design process - responding to the site, choosing orientation, sketching layout and massing - are 'crucial' in the real sense of the word. Good choices at this stage will allow a natural flow of sustainable design decisions to follow through to the details. Poor choices will ensure a continuing struggle, with one desperate stratagem after another being adopted to correct intrinsic problems. This state of affairs is likely to last for the lifetime of the building.

Choosing the right strategies depends on discovering early on what are the dominant issues for the project in hand. These will be determined largely by building type and site conditions. In a densely occupied office, set on an overshadowed inner city site, the need for light and ventilation may dominate. In a seaside development of housing for elderly people the priorities may be heating, views and sunshine. It depends also on assessing where investment in design time or in construction will produce the best return. There is little point in designing an elaborate and expensive heating control system for a building in which inappropriate glazing is going to cause overheating, and poor detailing will result in massive ventilation heat loss.

HOW SUSTAINABLE CAN YOU GET ?

Take a conventional building constructed to current Building Regulations standards as a base. It should be possible to achieve a very respectable improvement in sustainability - say 20 percent - with a modest design input. Advancing another 30 percent in sustainability is likely to involve considerable design time, and increases in capital costs as well. Achieving a 70 percent improvement may take the project into the realms of research and development, and demand a client who has a philosophical commitment to sustainability or wants to commission a landmark building.

No building can be completely green. There are degrees of sustainability, and the client with the design team must decide what is appropriate, what is feasible and what is affordable in the particular circumstances of the project in hand.

SOME GENERAL PRINCIPLES OF SUSTAINABLE DESIGN

- **An integrated approach will produce much better results than a piecemeal one.** There is no point in reducing the glazing ratio on north-facing facades, to control heat loss, if it means that artificial lighting has to be kept on all day. Not only will the lighting consume energy in itself; it may cause overheating which, in its turn, has to be countered by artificial cooling or ventilation.

- **Simple solutions are preferable to complexity and over-design.** It is better to provide just enough conventional glazing to meet daylighting needs, than to specify larger or smaller areas of high technology windows which need elaborate shading or daylighting devices.

- **The energy used during the life of a building is almost always much greater than the energy embodied in its fabric.** However, this is less true if fitting out is repeated in short cycles of five to fifteen years. It will also be less true of very low-energy buildings.

- **Saving energy is almost always more cost effective than producing or reclaiming it.** It is better to design a building with low heating demand than to use wind power to generate electricity to heat it, or a heat-pump to recover heat as it leaves the building in exhaust air.

- **The smaller a building's energy requirements, the greater the chance that renewable energy can effectively fill the gap.** For example, if a building cannot have opening windows, perhaps because of security or process requirements, designing a form and fabric which result in a low cooling load may mean that ground water can be used for cooling and refrigeration can be avoided.

- **Primary energy consumption, rather than consumption at point of use, is what matters .** About two thirds of the energy used to generate electricity goes to waste, so that a unit of electricity results in nearly three times as much CO_2 emissions as a unit of gas or oil used in an efficient boiler.

- **Many sustainable design decisions have a multiplier effect.** Simply specifying water-conserving bathroom taps, for example, reduces the demand on water supplies, reduces the load on sewage treatment plants, and saves on the energy used in both processes, as well as saving energy on hot-water heating in the building itself.

- **Design for durability is superior to design for recycling. And recycling is superior to waste.**

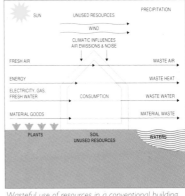

Wasteful use of resources in a conventional building.

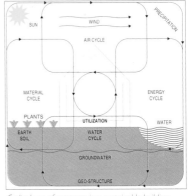

Cyclical use of resources in a sustainable building.
Source: GAIA Lista, Architects.

Architectural design has always been a matter of reconciling conflicting requirements and of trading off a benefit in one area against a drawback in another. Sustainable design is no exception.

- Smaller buildings use less materials, less energy, and cause less environmental impact. But tight spaces cannot easily accommodate change. This can lead to early obsolescence, which is environmentally undesirable.
- Low surface to volume ratio is usually more economical to build and uses less energy, unless it results in the building being so deep that it cannot be naturally ventilated, and so dark at its core that lights need to be kept on all day. Building form in dwellings - detached, semi-detached or terraced - can influence energy use by up to 50 percent.
- Planning efficiency effects capital costs, life cycle costs and energy use. For example, double-loaded corridors are better than single-loaded, unless the corridor has other functions - perhaps acting as a sun space, capturing solar gain and preheating ventilation air. Once plan shape is decided on, the consequences, for good or bad, are usually irreversible.
- Low glazing ratios minimise heat loss and reduce construction costs, but they also minimise daylight and may compromise the character and quality of the building. Glazing ratios cannot be changed after construction without major expenditure, and their impact is critical.

NOTES ON PART B

This part of the manual focuses essentially on architectural strategies. The sections on heating, lighting or ventilation have little to do with plant or pipe runs. They involve instead decisions on siting, form, mass and envelope, although this may not be apparent at first glance. As with almost any other aspect of architectural design, many of the implications of sustainability do not really become clear until worked through in the course of a project.

The guidance provided is necessarily general in nature, and it is for the design team to judge which strategies it is appropriate to adopt. Under most headings the differing requirements of domestic and non-domestic buildings are discussed, but it was not possible to cover the very wide range of variation found among non-domestic building types. Nor has any attempt been made to include case studies. However, in the suggestions for 'Further Reading' which accompany each section an effort has been made to identify publications which provide guidance relevant to specific building types, or which contain substantial case studies of completed projects.

Rules of thumb, short calculations and simple checking procedures thought likely to be helpful are included within the text. Many are based on fairly crude assumptions which make little allowance for particular or complex situations, but they can provide useful starting positions. Rules of thumb, which are probably the most user-friendly 'tool' at the early design stages, are the result of many years or decades of cumulative practical experience. Versions suitable for sustainable decision-making are scarce. Research is needed to develop more robust prediction models which produce useful results without critical dependence on precise assumptions. More sophisticated tools and techniques are covered in section C. 1.

FURTHER READING

GENERAL

- Baker, N.V. *Energy and Environment in Non-Domestic Buildings: a Technical Design Guide.* Cambridge, Cambridge Architectural Research Ltd. for the RIBA, 1995. 69 pp. A short guide to the principles of energy efficient building, by the team which developed the LT Method.

- Barnett, Dianna Lopez and William D. Browning. *A primer on sustainable building.* Rocky Mountain Institute, 1995. $16.95. Tel +1 303 927 3851 Fax +1 303 927 4178. Covers all of the issues and arguments in a very readable style aimed at professionals and interested laypersons.

- BS 8207:1985. *Code of Practice for Energy Efficiency in Buildings.* Amended February 1994. London, HMSO, 1994.

- Construction Industry Research and Information Association (CIRIA). *Environmental Handbook for Building and Civil Engineering Projects. Vol. 1, Design and Specification.* (SP 97) *Vol. 2, The Construction Phase.* (SP 98). London, CIRIA, c.1995 Fax. +44 171 222 1708. The first volume follows a plan-of-work sequence, covering each topic in one or two pages. Gives current best practice, legislation and sources of further information. UK data.

- *Going Green - The Green Construction Handbook: A Manual for Clients and Construction Professionals.* Research by Ove Arup & Partners. Bristol, JT Design Build Ltd., 1993. Fax +44 01272 290946. Covers the fundamental concepts of 'green' building and provides one-page summaries on generic systems and materials.

- Goulding, John R. , J. Owen Lewis, and Theo C. Steemers, Editors. *Energy in Architecture : The European Passive Solar Handbook* . London, Batsford for the Commission of the European Communities, 1992. IR£ 45. A comprehensive handbook based on design data, techniques and guidelines generated by EC-funded research and applications.

- Goulding, John R., J. Owen Lewis and Theo C. Steemers, Editors. *Energy Conscious Design - A Primer for Architects.* London, Batsford for the Commission of the European Communities, Batsford, 1992. IR£ 25 A well illustrated and easy-to-follow introduction to passive solar and energy-efficient design.

- Halliday, S. P.. *Environmental Code of Practice for Buildings and their Services.* Bracknell, Building Services Research and Information Association (BISRIA), 1994. 130 pp. £40.00. Fax +44 1344 487575. Step-by-step checklist for sustainable practice, following the sequence for a new building from inception to hand-over. It then continues with use, refurbishment, decommissioning, demolition and disposal. Aimed at clients, design teams and building managers.

- Thomas, Randall, Editor. *Environmental Design: An Introduction for Architects and Engineers.* London, Spon, 1996. Written by a team of specialists at Max Fordhams & Partners. Starts with some basic scientific principles, then covers air quality, noise, site planning, energy use, building materials and building form.

BUILDING TYPES

- Cambridge Architectural Research Limited. *Design Guides for Energy Efficient Non-Domestic Buildings.* Cambridge, Cambridge Architectural Research Ltd., 1994-95. A set of four to eight-page design guides and case studies for schools, colleges, offices, and hospitals. Available from BRECSU Enquiries Bureau, BRE, Garston, Watford, WD2 7JR. Tel +44 1923 664258 Fax +44 1923 664787.

- Durand, Eric. *Energy Efficiency in Hospitals and Clinics.* Paris, ADEME - OPET for the European Commission, 1993. 25 pp. Free. Guidelines and case studies. Available from: Energy Research Group, School of Architecture, University College Dublin, Richview, Clonskeagh, Dublin 14. Tel (01) 269 2750 Fax (01) 283 8908

- Durand, Eric. *Energy Efficiency in Office Buildings.* Paris, ADEME - OPET for the European Commission, 1993. 24 pp. Free. Guidelines and case studies. Available from: Energy Research Group, School of Architecture, University College Dublin, Richview, Clonskeagh, Dublin 14. Tel (01) 269 2750 Fax (01) 283 8908

- Hastings, S. R.. editor. *Passive Solar Commercial and Institutional Buildings: a Sourcebook of Examples and Design Insights.* Chichester, John Wiley & Sons, for the International Energy Agency, 1994.

- Instituto de la Mediana y Pequena Industria Valenciana. *Rational Use of Energy in the Hotel Sector.* IMPIVA for the European Commission, 1995. 19 pp. Free. Guidelines and case studies.

- Nisson, J. D. Ned and Guatam Dutt. *The Superinsulated Home Book.* John Wiley & Sons, 1985. Out of print.

- O'Cofaigh, Eoin, John Olley and J. Owen Lewis. *The Climatic Dwelling: an Introduction to Climate Responsive Residential Architecture.* London, James and James (Science Publishers) Ltd., 1996. IR£30. Principles, guidelines and case studies

- Talbott, John L. *Simply Build Green: A Technical Guide to the Ecological Houses at the Findhorn Foundation.* Findhorn, Findhorn Foundation Development Wing, 1993. ISBN 0 905249 86 0

- UK. Department of the Environment. Energy Efficiency Office. Best Practice Programme. *Good Practice Guides* and *Case Studies.* A useful series of booklets on a range of building types, covering new build and refurbishment. Available from Enquiries Bureau, BRECSU, Building Research Establishment, Garston, Watford WD2 7JR, UK. Tel +44 1923 664258 Fax +44 1293 664097

- UK. Department of the Environment. Energy Efficiency Office. *Energy Efficiency in Buildings : Sports Buildings; Shops; Catering Establishments; Schools; Hotels; Health Care Buildings; Further and Higher Education Buildings.,* London, Energy Efficiency Office, 1989 - 1993. A series of 18 - 24 page booklets, each covering a particular building type.

- Yannas, Simos, Editor. *Housing Examples.* (Module 2: Building Typologies and Examples). Published under a TEMPUS Joint European Project: Building Science and Environment-Conscious Design. London, Architectural Association School of Architecture for the European Commission, 1993. A collection of case studies.

HEALTH & COMFORT

The goal in a sustainably designed building is the same as in a conventional one; to provide comfortable conditions for the people who use it. Because the objective is to expand the role of form and fabric in moderating the climate, designers need to be sensitive to the complex interactions between external climate, building fabric and the human body. This Section outlines the sustainable view of human comfort in buildings.

Mallow Street Apartments, Limerick, Murray O'Laoire

'Natural' techniques can not only match, but improve on, the levels of comfort provided by artificial systems. Issues which in a conventional building could be left to the services consultant are taken on board by the whole design team.

It is widely felt that in the 1970s and 1980s we were over specifying services, demanding a high degree of control within very tight tolerances. Conventional comfort standards, such as those given in ISO 7730, are based on studies carried out in climate laboratories. Field studies suggest that their predictions may not be entirely reliable. For example, optimum comfort temperature is often over-estimated in calculating heating requirements and under-estimated in calculating cooling loads. This wastes energy. One reason for the discrepancy may be that laboratory-based methods underestimate peoples' adaptive responses and their need for some variety in their environment. 'Adaptive responses' are the actions people take to make themselves more comfortable; taking off a jacket, opening or closing blinds, changing position, or taking a cool drink.

Building Regulations and Health and Safety at Work Regulations offer little guidance on comfort. Discussion tends to be in terms of avoiding hazards to health, rather than creating conditions which are positively comfortable and enjoyable.

Recommended temperatures, relative humidities and air velocities in different rooms in residential buildings. Source: ISO 7730 (1984)				
Room	Temp °C	Temp. diff. (K) walls - room floor - room	Relative humidity	Air velocity m/s
Living room	21		Summer:	Summer: 0.25
Bathroom	22	<3	30 - 70%	
Bedroom	18			
Toilets	18		Winter:	Winter: 0.15
Stairs/Halls	16		<50%	

I   THE OCCUPANTS

Context has a critical effect on peoples' perceptions of comfort. A level of daylight that would be considered 'gloomy' in an office on a green-field suburban site may be perfectly acceptable in an overshadowed inner-city building.

It is also increasingly clear that if conditions in a building are natural rather than artificial, and people have some degree of control over their own territory, they have a much more relaxed attitude to variations in the interior climate. Glare caused by the sun is somehow less offensive than glare from a light fitting, and the 'breeze' from the window opened by oneself might have been interpreted as a 'draught' if it had come from a central air-handling system.

Comfort is a subjective sensation and no set of conditions will satisfy all occupants simultaneously. In sustainable design it is now usual to take account of people's adaptive behaviour and to allow them some degree of control over their immediate environment. This permits a wider range of tolerances than might have been usual under traditional codes of practice. However, there are still situations where tight tolerances must be maintained; for example where the occupants are very young or very old, are ill or are confined to a fixed position.

2   THERMAL COMFORT

Thermal comfort depends on the balance between heat gains from the internal metabolism of the body and heat losses to its environment. People get uncomfortable if the body loses heat too quickly or too slowly. Some of the parameters - air temperature, mean radiant temperature, air speed and humidity - are environmental. Others - activity level, clothing, body weight, subjective factors and adaptation - are personal.

The mean radiant temperature of room surfaces is as important for comfort as the air temperature. An increase in mean radiant temperature allows comfort conditions to be achieved at lower air temperatures, and a reduction of 1°C in air temperature may save up to 10 percent of energy consumption. Poorly-insulated buildings have cold interior surfaces and need higher air temperatures to compensate. So insulation saves energy not only by reducing building heat loss, but also by reducing design air temperatures.

People can be made very uncomfortable by radiant asymmetry, where one surface has a radiant temperature significantly different from others in the room. Single-glazed windows, cold floors and overhead heat sources are common culprits. Abnormal differences in air temperature between head and feet also cause discomfort. A difference of more than 3°C should be avoided, and warmer feet are preferred.

Ireland's high relative humidities tend to be a problem only in under-heated buildings in winter, where 'dampness' increases discomfort. If the air is heated it rarely becomes too dry. It is very unusual for the weather to get so hot that the high relative humidity causes discomfort for people outdoors. Inside buildings, winter or summer, high rates of occupancy and processes which generate moisture can, of course, produce uncomfortably high humidity levels. This can almost always be resolved by local extraction and /or increased ventilation rates.

The higher the air speed the greater the rate of body heat loss through convection and evaporation. This has implications for ventilation and for infiltration.

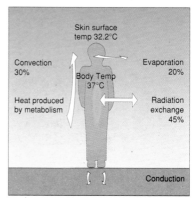

Heat balance of the human body

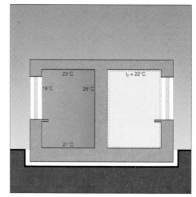

The concept of mean radiant temperature (t_r)

3   VISUAL COMFORT

Poor lighting can cause eyestrain, fatigue, headaches and irritability, to say nothing of mistakes and accidents. For visual comfort people need the right intensity and direction of illumination for the task they are engaged in, together with pleasant ambient lighting. They need good colour rendering, freedom from glare and some variety in lighting quality.

Tables listing recommended illuminances for different activities, such as those appearing in the lighting guides published by the Chartered Institution of Building Services Engineers (CIBSE), are familiar to designers. Under pressure from rising energy costs, and following results of research into human visual performance, many countries have reduced their recommended lighting levels in recent years. It has been found that where the source of light is natural people tolerate a wider range of illuminance values.

4   ACOUSTIC COMFORT

Acoustic quality is not a primary issue in sustainable design but the acoustic consequences of 'green' strategies have to be taken into account. Natural ventilation implies open windows and, sometimes, ventilation openings between interior spaces. Obtrusive traffic noise or loss of sound privacy are not acceptable by-products. If carpeting is omitted to limit the problem of house dust mites, or to allow the structure to act as a thermal store, other measures may have to be taken to reduce the transmission of impact noise and provide enough sound absorption in occupied spaces.

5   AIR QUALITY

Compared with the other parameters of comfort this is the one about which there is the most uncertainty. Provided that the outdoor air is of acceptable quality the traditional problems of stuffiness and odour can be resolved by ventilation. Radon build-up, in areas where it is known to be a risk, can be prevented by sealing solid floors or providing sub-floor ventilation. Other known hazards, such as Humidifier fever, Legionnaire's Disease, mould growth, fumes from the office copier or from an underground car park, can be eliminated by good design and maintenance practices.

The symptoms of Sick Building Syndrome appear to be short-lived. They tend to develop after a short stay in the building, get worse during the day, but quite quickly disappear after the person leaves the building. This repeated discomfort is bad enough, but the greater worry is long term damage to health. Many people spend 80 to 90 percent of their lives inside buildings, and the impact of constant exposure to low level emissions from the wide variety of materials commonly found in buildings today is unknown. The rapid rise in asthmatic illnesses among children and teenagers is another cause for concern. Reducing infiltration to conserve energy means that dust and emission concentrations in the air are likely to rise. This increases the need for care in the specification of materials and in the design of ventilation systems.

COMMON INDOOR AIR CONTAMINANTS

- Asbestos fibre

- Formaldehyde vapour

- Volatile Organic Compounds (VOC's)

- Tobacco smoke

- Radon gas

---

6   DESIGN TEAM POLICY

The benefits of accepting wider tolerances are substantial. One study of an air-conditioned office building demonstrated that reducing lighting and power specifications, and designing the air-conditioning for 22°C plus or minus 2.5°C instead of 21° plus or minus 1°, would reduce both capital and running costs and halve CO_2 emissions . (Burton, 1993)

Not enough is yet known about which aspects of comfort allow room for manoeuvre, or which kinds of systems can best accommodate individual control. It might be prudent to work to conventional standards, but to allow wider tolerances, and provide back-up systems for when conditions fall outside acceptable limits. It is clearly essential to make this strategy explicit and agree it with the client at the outset.

Formaldehyde emissions from a variety of construction materials, furnishings and consumer products. (Data from ASHRAE)	
Materials / Products	**Range of Formaldehyde emission rates µg / m² / day**
Medium - density fiberboard	17,600 - 55,000
Hardwood plywood panelling	1,500 - 34,000
Particleboard	2,000 - 25,000
Urea - formaldehyde foam insulation	1,200 - 19,200
Softwood plywood	240 - 720
Paper products	260 - 680
Fiberglass products	400 - 470
Clothing	35 - 570
Resilient flooring	<240
Carpeting	NP[a] - 65
Upholstery fabric	NP - 7
[a]NP = None Present	

Source: Balaras, 1993

FURTHER READING

- *A Review of Indoor Air Quality and its Impact on the Health and Well-being of Office Workers.* Brussels, European Commission, Directorate General for Employment, Industrial Relations and Social Affairs, 1992. 109 pp.

- *Guidelines for Ventilation Requirements in Buildings,* (Report 11, European Collaborative Action - Indoor Air Quality and its Impact on Man.) Brussels, European Commission, Directorate General for Employment, Industrial Relations and Social Affairs, 1992. 36pp. Guidance on risks and standards for various indoor pollutants, building types and occupancy rates.

- *Healthy Materials.* Canada Mortgage and Housing Corporation, P.O. Box 3077, Markham, Ontario, Canada L3R 6G4. $35.00 p.a. Bi-annual publication covering international developments in materials emission research, standards and application.

- *Sick Building Syndrome: A Practical Guide.* (Report 4, European Collaborative Action - Indoor Air Quality and its Impact on Man.) Luxembourg, European Commission, 1989. 36pp. Risk factors associated with various indoor pollutants, with guidelines, checklists and questionnaires for conducting building investigations.

CLIMATE

Information on climate has always been necessary for good building design. If the objective is to maximise the contribution of renewable energies, then access to good and relevant climate data becomes critical. The information presented in this Section should be sufficient to give the designer a qualitative understanding of the Irish climate and its implications for sustainable design. However, for detailed design calculations, and more particularly for computer simulation, full statistical tables would be necessary.

The key climate data requirements for sustainable design in Ireland are, unsurprisingly, air temperature, solar radiation, wind speed and wind direction. Other climate factors play a contributory role.

Some climate phenomena have fairly stable patterns, while others show wide variations, or are quite unpredictable. The mean monthly air temperature for any location in Ireland is very stable from year to year, but mean monthly sunshine or rainfall can differ from one year to the next by a factor of two. For design purposes a critical issue is not just the range, but also the time scale. For example, long term averages are taken over 30 years. If the intention were simply to save energy over the design life of the building, then day-to-day fluctuations in air temperature would not matter. If human comfort is an issue, then they matter very much indeed.

It must be stressed that the local climate at any site is the result of interaction between regional climate and local features such as topography, vegetation and existing buildings. All of the maps should be read in this light. Some climate parameters - sunlight and wind direction, for example - are more subject to local modification than others. The designer can start by establishing the climatic character of the region (the macroclimate) and use that information to suggest initial design responses. Early strategic proposals can be refined in the light of subsequent microclimatic and site analyses.

This section deals with macroclimate and the extent to which it is modified by local topography and other factors to produce microclimate. Detailed site analysis is covered in Section B.3 : Site.

Selected climate data for eight locations are given in Appendix 7. Published meteorological data can often be supplemented. The Meteorological Service may be able to provide additional information on particular locations. For projects with long lead times, it can sometimes be useful to take a series of on-site readings of climate factors relevant to the type of development proposed. Local knowledge and on-site assessment can, as always, provide useful clues.

I   AIR TEMPERATURE

The annual mean daily air temperature for Ireland is about 10°C. Temperatures tend to be 1°C higher in the south-west half of the country and 1°C lower in the north-east or at inland locations. Air temperatures are lower at higher altitudes (by about 0.6°C for every 100m above sea level), and urban areas tend to be warmer than open country.

Compared with a continental climate the differences between maximum and minimum temperatures, whether on a daily or an annual basis, are very modest. The number of days when the temperature does not rise above 0°C averages only one per year, though the incidence can vary from zero days in one year to five in the next. Occasions where the temperature remains above 26.6°C for a full 24 hours are rare.

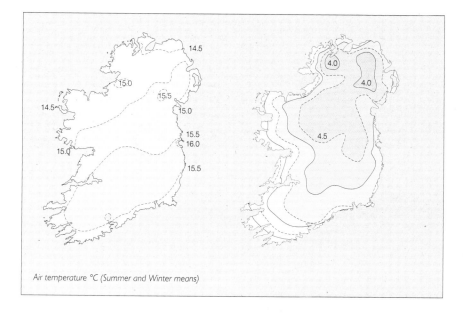

Air temperature °C (Summer and Winter means)

Winter design temperatures, which are used to determine peak heating demand, are mild: -1 deg C for Dublin and -2 deg C at Shannon. (These compare with - 7 deg C for Copenhagen, -16 deg C for Munich, and -2 deg C for Marseilles.)

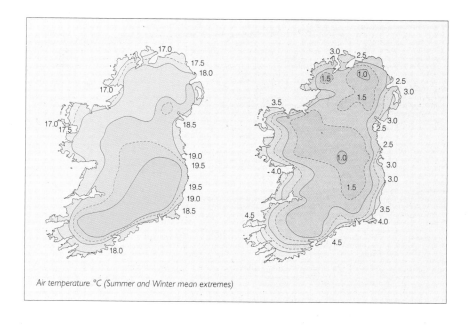

Air temperature °C (Summer and Winter mean extremes)

Because of these moderate temperatures, solar energy can make a substantial contribution to building energy requirements, and artificial cooling should rarely be necessary. Although the heating season is a long one, the temperature difference to be made up at any time is relatively small.

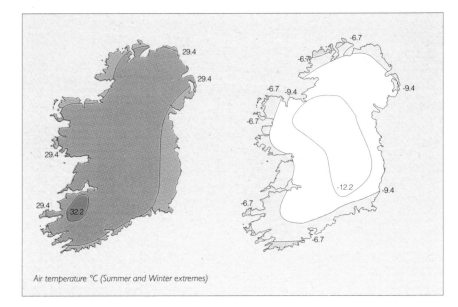

Air temperature °C (Summer and Winter extremes)

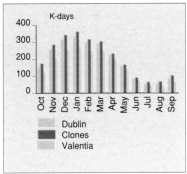

Monthly values for heating degree days at Dublin, Clones and Valentia

Heating degree day figures do show regional variations. Dublin has 2100 degree-days, compared to 2414 for the coldest and 1825 for the warmest locations in the country. Year-to-year variations are generally within plus or minus 15 percent of the long-term average. Degree-days for built-up areas tend to be somewhat lower than for open sites. A reduction of ten percent can be made for the centres of towns. For elevated sites, two degree-days can be added for each additional metre above sea level.

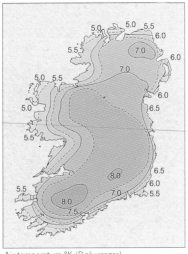

Air temperature °K (Daily ranges)

2   WIND

Ireland is one of the windiest parts of Europe. Mean and maximum airspeeds are both high. There are pronounced variations in wind speeds on coasts and on high ground and wide variations also in prevailing wind direction from place to place. Wind speeds tend to be greater during the day than at night. The variation over periods of four to seven days, associated with the passing of weather fronts, is greater than the variation from month to month. Mean wind speeds in towns and cities tend to be lower than in rural areas.

Wind speed and direction have a substantial impact on site microclimate and on building energy demands. Wind speed modifies air temperatures, and can rapidly remove surface heat generated by the sun. On the positive side, wind is a good disperser of air pollution.

For well insulated parts of a building the influence of wind is relatively small. The impact on window heat losses is more significant, especially for single glazing. Wind driven ventilation losses are critical, but information on actual ventilation rates in buildings on sites of varying exposure and in differing wind climates is not available.

Mean annual wind speed (m/s)

The landscape exerts a powerful influence on the wind microclimate. Wind speed is reduced by the frictional resistance offered by the landscape. The rougher the terrain, the greater the reduction. The prevailing wind direction may be S, SW, SE, S, or NW in different parts of country, but in any one place the frequency of winds from different directions is strongly influenced by local topography. Hills and valleys, water, trees and other vegetation, and existing buildings can have radical impact on wind direction. Site specific information is important for building orientation and shelter.

There is excellent potential for harnessing wind on hilly or coastal sites and also on low, level inland sites such as bogs. Figures shown in meteorological records are at nominal ground level (10m). For high altitudes and particular land configurations the values may be much greater. For wind power generation, the critical figure is the percentage of time during which wind speeds fall within the operating limits for the equipment. The *CEC European Wind Atlas* includes techniques for estimating the potential wind resource at a particular site.

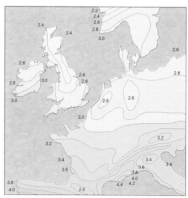

Wind direction frequency

3   SOLAR RADIATION

Solar radiation is the primary factor influencing all other climate behaviour. It is also the primary source of renewable energy for buildings in Ireland. It offers opportunities for active and passive heating, for photovoltaic power generation and, importantly, for daylighting.

Global solar radiation in Ireland averages 950 kWh/m^2 per year. This compares with 1300 kWh/m^2 in central Italy. The figure does not vary much across the country, and the maximum variation is plus or minus 10 percent. Radiation during December is low, but it is reasonably high during those months of spring and autumn which fall within the heating season. For any particular month there is a pronounced variation from year to year

About 60 percent of the radiation is diffuse and 40 percent is direct. Cloud cover, turbidity and air pollution all reduce radiation. A high proportion of radiation is diffuse. In cloudy conditions diffuse radiation is greater than direct radiation for all surfaces, so it is worth trying to harness both.

A horizontal surface receives more radiation in summer and less in winter. The amount of radiation received on sloping ground is influenced by its angle of inclination and its orientation. On a sunny winter day a 20° south-facing slope will receive twice as much energy as a horizontal surface in the same location. In clear weather, irradiation values for south facing vertical surfaces reach their maximum in early March, fall to a summer minimum in June, reach a secondary peak in mid-October and then drop to a winter minimum in January. The drop in June results from the fact that the sun's rays in midsummer are at a sharper angle to any vertical surface and so have less effect.

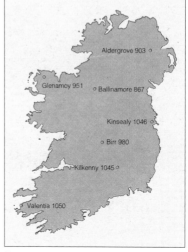

Average daily solar radiation in Europe. (kWh/m^2/day)

Solar radiation, even for comparatively short periods, can produce high surface temperatures in exposed building materials. On a hot sunny day with an air temperature of 25°C some typical values would be:

Pitched roof with black covering facing South	100°C
Clear glass over dark insulated background	70°C
Flat roof	70°C
Insulated black metal behind clear glass	125°C

On a clear night in winter one can safely assume that the minimum surface temperature of these materials would be -15°C. These wide thermal variations and ultra-violet light combine to produce severe weathering conditions for materials and components on any south facing surface.

Solar radiation in Ireland (kWh/m^2/year)

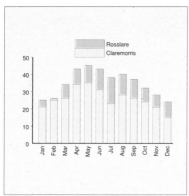

Sunshine *(Percentage amounts of maximum possible between sunrise and sunset at Rosslare and Claremorris)*

4   SUNLIGHT

Sunlight amounts in Ireland are moderate, being about half those of southern Europe. The probability of sunlight varies from an average of about 30 percent of the hours between sunrise and sunset in the north-west, to 35 percent in the south-east. The variation from year to year is considerable. Probability is higher during the summer months. Rosslare, for example, gets 40 percent of maximum possible sunshine in June and 20 percent in December. There are no data associating probability with direction. Sky turbidity and air purity, both of which have an impact on sunlight intensity, vary with geographic location.

In Belfast, the longest day is 17 hrs and the shortest 7 hrs, with maximum sun angles of 59° and 12° respectively. The corresponding figures for Dublin are 16 hrs 45 mins and 7 hrs 15 mins for length of day, with maximum sun angles of 60° and 13°. For Valentia the figures are 16 hrs 30 mins and 7 hrs 30 mins, with maximum sun angles of 61.5° and 14.5°. At the March and September equinoxes the maximum sun angle is approximately 37°.

Because of the geometric behaviour of the sun, it is relatively easy to establish by graphical methods whether, and for what part of the day, any part of a site can receive sunlight (see Section C.1: Tools for Design and Evaluation, and Appendix 2).

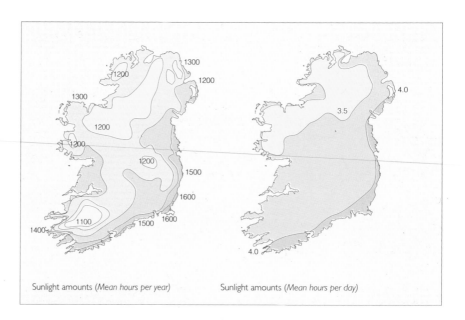

Sunlight amounts *(Mean hours per year)*   Sunlight amounts *(Mean hours per day)*

5   CLOUD COVER

Cloud cover inhibits incoming short-wave radiation from the sun, reducing air temperatures and daylight levels. But it also inhibits outgoing long-wave radiation to the atmosphere, and so reduces heat losses from the ground and from buildings, particularly from sloping or horizontal glazing.

Ireland's fairly high levels of cloudiness show modest variation from month to month, with most areas having minimum cloudiness in April and maximum in July. In all areas there is less cloud at night than during daylight hours.

6   AIR POLLUTION

Air pollution reduces the amount of solar radiation reaching the site. Pollutants absorb and scatter solar radiation, decreasing the strength of direct radiation and, under clear sky conditions, increasing the amount of diffuse radiation. In addition, by forming a deposit on glass, pollutants reduce the transmission capability of windows and of transparent collector surfaces. Heat gain and daylighting are both affected. Poor air quality also limits the possibilities for natural ventilation.

Still air conditions in urban areas can lead to considerable accumulations of pollutants in the atmosphere. Inversions are also liable to develop in valleys during the winter, trapping pollutants within them. On most sites, however, day to day variation in solar radiation depends more on the source of the meteorological air masses moving over the site. Polar and North Atlantic air masses tend to be clean. Continental air masses may accumulate heavy burdens of particles and pollutants, especially when wind speeds are low. Information on prevailing wind directions in relation to major pollutant sources is useful for site selection.

In recent years, data on concentrations of smoke, sulphur dioxide, nitrous oxides, lead and ground-level ozone have been collected. There is no nation-wide grid of monitoring stations, and sampling of different pollutants is patchy. There is not yet enough statistical evidence to draw general conclusions, but some of the smaller cities, where no smoke controls have been introduced, appear to have more severe smoke-related pollution than does Dublin. Traffic generated pollution is a growing problem.

7   RELATIVE HUMIDITY

Relative humidities in Ireland tend to be high; seldom below 80 percent and often above 90 percent. Conditions of high temperature combined with high humidity, which would have to be corrected by air-conditioning, are unusual however. Low temperature combined with low humidity is also rare. As a result, winter comfort can normally be achieved simply by raising the air temperature, and summer air-conditioning in most buildings is unnecessary.

8   GROUND TEMPERATURE

Ground temperatures are relevant for heat losses from buildings which are in contact with the soil, or partially or totally embedded in it. They are also relevant for systems in which outdoor air is pre-heated or pre-cooled by being drawn through the earth.

Ground temperatures (measured at 50 to 100 mm depth) and earth temperatures (0.3 to 1.2m depth) are very dependent on local soil and climate conditions and should only be applied locally. The annual variation in temperature decreases with distance from the surface, and at 3m the temperature remains constant throughout the year. In urban areas ground temperatures tend to be higher.

9   EVAPORATION RATES

Variations in rainfall and wind speed, coupled with slight variations in temperature and relative humidity, can produce a pronounced geographical variation in the rate of evaporation of moisture from buildings or ground surfaces. January rates of evaporation are about 15 percent of July rates, and evaporation rates in the West of Ireland are significantly lower than in the East. A well insulated cavity-walled building will not be affected, but the rate of heat loss through a solid wall will increase with saturation.

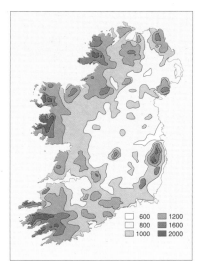
Rainfall amounts (mm)

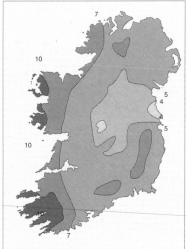
Driving rain index (m²/s)

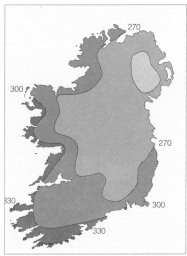
Grass-growing season (Days)

10   RAINFALL

Rainfall amounts in Ireland are medium to high, with a pronounced increase from East to West and from low to high ground. The difference between seasons is moderate, with December generally being the wettest month and April the driest. Rain showers are relatively light, frequent and unpredictable.

This rainfall pattern is one of the factors which contributes to Ireland's potential for the production of sustainable timber for construction use, and the generation of energy from biomass crops.

Local variations will have effects on the rate of growth of shelter belts, trees planted for shading, earth roofs, or any other vegetation planted for design purposes.

11   DRIVING RAIN

The Driving-rain Index indicates the severity of the climate in terms of wind and rain combined. Most practitioners are aware that conditions tend to be more severe on the West Coast or on high ground, and make provision for this in their detailed design.

Local experience, which takes account of terrain, airflows and building shapes, may be a better basis for design decisions than any analytical process.

12   GROWING SEASON

The length of the frost-free and growing seasons have implications for the survival and the growth rate of vegetation planted for shade or shelter. Local topographical features can modify temperatures at a particular site. A difference of one or two degrees from the winter regional average can have a marked effect on the viability of many species.

There are large variations in the dates of first and last frosts, and the length of the frost-free season ranges from about 195 days in the Southeast to 105 days in the worst inland sites. The length of the grass-growing season varies from approximately 240 days in the north-east to 330 days in the south-west. It is the long growing season which makes biomass potentially viable as an energy resource in Ireland.

FURTHER READING

- Rohan, P. K.. *The Climate of Ireland.* 2nd ed. Dublin, Stationery Office, 1986.

SITE

Site and microclimate - important elements in the design of any building - are crucial in sustainable design. Decisions on how to use the site, if indeed it should be built on at all, establish the base on which all later design decisions rest. The site provides the context for the buildings, but the buildings in turn modify the site. The local ecosystem is altered, habitats changed and flows of energy, water, nutrients and pollutants modified. Neighbouring buildings and distant communities are affected. This Section deals with site analysis and with response to, or modification of, site microclimate. It should be read in conjunction with Section B.2: Climate

How does sustainable site use differ from conventional site planning, when most of the factors to be considered are common to both? Sustainable design takes account of the impact of site decisions on people and places distant from the site. It exploits or manipulates site characteristics so as to reduce energy consumption in the building, while still providing comfortable living conditions. It tackles ordinary site problems in sustainable rather than conventional ways. Rainwater is let percolate into the ground instead of being channelled into a sewer. Biological techniques are used to clean a contaminated site. Finally, in sustainable design all of these issues are seen as interdependent.

The site has a history - geological, biological, social and cultural. It has its own ecology and microclimate. It may have natural or man-made hazards. Its aesthetic qualities may be good, bad or indifferent. But every site has resources, to be exploited rather than consumed. The approach should be creative. To design and build solely in response to the existing conditions is to miss an opportunity. Sustainable development provides a chance to upgrade not only the site itself but also its neighbourhood, and to make a contribution, however small, to protecting global resources.

I   THE SITE AS FOUND

Obtain as much information as possible from published and official sources and supplement it with local knowledge and site investigations. There is considerable overlap between sustainable site analysis and the preparation of an Environmental Impact Statement under the EC (Environmental Impact Assessment) Regulations. The Environmental Protection Agency's *Advice Notes on Current Practice* provides a useful checklist of issues and impacts that covers many, but not all, of the concerns of sustainable architecture. A lot can be learned from the site itself; its historical uses, the condition of existing structures, the type and health of vegetation.

Consider the following 'sustainable' questions.

*   What is the regional macroclimate ? Is it modified by the altitude or topography of the site? What is the degree of exposure - is the site on open territory, or in the centre of a built-up area?
*   What is the slope and orientation of the site? Because the rays of the sun are at a greater angle to its surface, a south facing slope receives more solar radiation than a level site. This is particularly significant during the winter, when the sun angle is low.
*   Are there hills, trees or nearby buildings which will obstruct sunlight or daylight, or provide shelter from prevailing winds? Is there the possibility that in the future there may be obstructions on neighbouring sites? Sunlight (direct beam solar radiation) and diffuse light (solar radiation scattered by atmosphere, cloud or pollution) need to be considered separately. It is obvious that the orientation and slope of the site, and overshadowing by hills, trees or existing buildings, affect sunlight availability. However, large or nearby obstructions, even to the North of the site, will also reduce the amount of diffuse light received from the sky.

Since sun and wind are two of the most important climate factors, and both can be radically affected by local conditions, it is worth taking the time to establish how they behave on the site. For many sites it is a simple exercise to plot overshadowing on site sections, using maximum and minimum sun angles and the points of mid-winter and mid-summer sunrise and sunset. In more complex cases graphic tools, physical models, or software can be used. Some methods for assessing sunlight and wind patterns are described in Section C.1: Tools for Design and Evaluation.

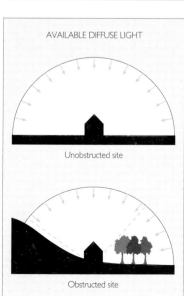

AVAILABLE DIFFUSE LIGHT

Unobstructed site

Obstructed site

*   Where is the water table and what is the pattern of existing drainage on the site? Are there any lakes, ponds or streams on the site? Is there ground water that can usefully be tapped ? What is the soil type? Are soil and water of good quality, or are they polluted?
*   Is the air quality good enough and the noise level low enough to permit opening windows and natural ventilation ?
*   What is the pattern of vegetation on the site; trees, shrubs, shelter belts, crops, ground cover?
*   What is the potential for solar, wind or hydro power?
*   Is there space for on-site waste recycling or digestion, for permaculture, for biomass or food production?
*   Are there any hazards on the site; contaminated soil or ground water, radon or electromagnetic radiation sources? Until the debate about the latter is settled, it is probably better not to build within 30m of high-tension power lines, transformers or microwave transmitters.
*   Are there historical, cultural, or archaeological features which ought to be preserved ? Are there flora or fauna which ought to be protected ? Does the landscape make an aesthetic contribution to the locality? Is there a distinctive sense of place which should be respected?
*   Are there existing structures which can be re-used, building materials which can be re-cycled ? Can soil, stone or timber on the site be used for construction, for landscaping, for shelter ?

- If it is a residential project, are shops, schools, churches and hospitals within reach by public transport ? If the proposal is for a commercial project, can workers get there by public transport ? Are there existing services and utilities which can be tapped into ?
- Finally, if the site has not already been purchased, should it be built on at all? Other things being equal, it is better to site a building in an area where the infrastructure of utilities, roads, transport, and social, cultural, commercial and community systems already exists. The building and its users benefit from the support systems. The loss of agricultural or recreational land, the destruction of habitats, and the waste of materials are reduced. The pollution caused by constructing and using new roads, power, water and waste disposal systems is avoided. Bringing an abandoned or contaminated industrial site back into healthy use, is even better. If a green-field site must be used, try to preserve as much unbuilt site as possible.

Protect or create wildlife habitats

2   SUSTAINABLE SITE STRATEGIES

In an ideal world the design team would be consulted before the site is selected. In reality this almost never happens. The team may find itself with a site, brief and budget which allow very little room for manoeuvre and, on the face of it, no opportunity at all to indulge in adventurous sustainable design moves. In fact, there is no site which does not provide sustainable design opportunities, and sustainable thinking applied to unpromising situations can have surprisingly good results.

Creative manipulation of a site's microclimate can enhance the energy performance of the building, the levels of comfort, health and enjoyment in interior and exterior spaces, and the impact of the project on the planet as a whole. The objective is to create the best possible conditions for the building and its occupants, and the most positive interaction with the wider environment.

Exploit sun, shelter and topography

Establishing shelter, for example, frees a building or settlement to take advantage of other opportunities. A farmhouse might be sited on a rise to survey its land. A belt of trees provides shelter. Inside this enclosure the house no longer needs to turn its back to the prevailing south-westerly winds, but can enlarge its windows and turn to face the sun. A 'window' carefully cut in the shelter belt provides a distant view. On an urban site the shelter may be provided by other buildings, but the same principles apply.

In most cases, the sensation of comfort or pleasure outdoors depends, as it does indoors, on the quality of light, on sunshine and shade, shelter from the wind, materials that hold and release warmth, and on the acoustic qualities of the space. Of course, shelter is not always appropriate. Exposure to wind and spray may be part of the authentic experience at a coastal interpretative centre.

Buildings or boundary walls create immediate shelter, but for many elements of microclimate time is an essential ingredient. The first planting on an exposed site will be of robust species that can withstand severe winds or, perhaps, heavy pollution. As that first planting matures it will create conditions of soil, water, shade and shelter which make a friendly habitat for less hardy varieties, and for fauna which could not have occupied the site before. These in their turn trigger further change, and so the cycle continues. The exotic and beautiful gardens on the once barren island of Garinish in Co. Kerry are a classic example.

Development density is a very complex issue. For example, terraced housing is economical in its use of materials and of land. If oriented in the right direction, it can make quite effective use of solar gain. The detached single-family house, on the other hand, is usually wasteful of land, energy and materials, but offers greater opportunities for solar gain, rainwater collection, composting or crop growing. The variations from site to site, and between different building types, are so great that any generalisations should be treated with great caution.

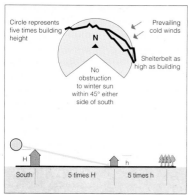

Solar site selector. Based on Hall and Warm, 1995

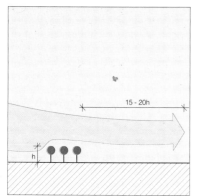

Natural shelter belts: extent of sheltered zone

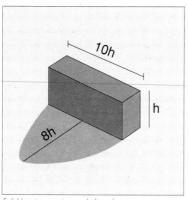

Solid barrier: maximum sheltered zone

2.1 Exploit Sunlight and Daylight

Unobstructed slopes facing within 45° of south tend to be good for solar gain. Slopes over 10° facing within 45° of north present difficulties for passive solar design. Superinsulated construction combined with clerestory lighting may be a better option. However, the outdoor space to the south of such a building may be protected from both northern and prevailing winds. If possible, locate the building where it will be free of overshadowing on all sides. Freedom from overshadowing during the hours around solar noon (in Winter, 12.25 pm in the East and 12.40 pm in the West of Ireland) is particularly important for any facade which is to function as a solar collector.

Light-coloured finishes on ground and vertical surfaces reflect more light and will contribute to higher levels of daylight within the building.

2.2 Use or Create Shelter

Avoid placing buildings in very exposed positions; hilltops, bottoms of valleys, north-facing slopes, or parts of the site unprotected from prevailing winds. Creating shelter on the site can cut heat loss from buildings by up to 15 percent and reduce the wind-chill factor for people outdoors (Barton Davis Guise, 1995).

Reducing wind speeds generally raises air temperatures. The most effective shelter is provided by a permeable or semi-permeable barrier. A solid barrier, such as a wall, reduces wind speed immediately downwind, at the cost of some turbulence. But the wind recovers 50 percent of its strength at a distance about five times the height of the barrier. A permeable shelter belt creates less turbulence in its lee and is effective for a distance about 15 to 20 times its height.

For a screen of limited width - a building for example - the sheltered zone increases in depth from the corners of the building. The depth of the protected zone increases with building width until the width is about ten times the building height. At this point the maximum depth of the sheltered zone is about eight times the building height.

On a sloping site a shelter belt can be used to divert the cold which flows downhill at night. If it obstructs the sun, however, it may create a frost pocket instead.

2.3 Take Advantage of Thermal Mass

Dark coloured materials absorb more heat, and so raise air temperatures near their surfaces. Materials of high thermal mass - concrete, brick or stone, for example - store heat and release it as air temperatures drop, so reduce temperature swings. Water heats and cools even more slowly, so the presence of a body of water has a greater moderating effect.

2.4 Screen or Absorb Noise

Earth berms, buildings, and other solid objects are the best barriers for sound reduction. However, a dense belt of vegetation scatters, diffuses and alters the spectrum of noise. Noise barriers work both ways, protecting the site from a noisy environment or protecting the locality from noise on the site.

Ground cover, and climbers or creepers on wall surfaces, absorb sound, changing the acoustic quality of outdoor spaces.

2.5   Use or Create Natural Shade

Deciduous trees used to screen the sun in summer and filter light in winter can be effective in reducing glare and excessive heat gain in a building. However, even in winter, deciduous trees reduce the available daylight light to between 40 and 50 percent of its unobstructed value. Trees in leaf reduce it to 10 or 20 percent of the unobstructed value. The effect depends on the species. Trees with a tall, clean trunk and high-level canopy will screen mid-day summer sun, while allowing low-angle winter sun to reach the building.

Outdoors, air temperatures under a stand of trees or a dense layer of vegetation are modified. The area is shaded from the sun during the day, and protected against radiation to the sky at night.

2.6   Absorb Air Pollution

Vegetation absorbs carbon dioxide and emits oxygen. It takes one-to-two hectares of trees, depending on the species, to absorb and process the CO_2 produced by the average house. Trees and shrubs can remove up to 75 percent of dust, lead and other particulates from the air.

2.7   Protect Water Resources

Ensure that as much rainwater as possible finds its way back into the soil, and in as clean a condition as possible. Try to follow natural drainage patterns on the site. Minimise the extent of impervious surfaces such as driveways, parking, and paving. This helps to maintain the water table and slows run-off, reducing damage to neighbouring land and waterways, or the load on a local sewage system. If the site is large enough, detention ponds can be used to delay runoff of storm water. Avoid contaminating ground water at all costs. Once polluted, it tends to remain so for many years. Septic tanks and uncontained waste are two of the most common culprits.

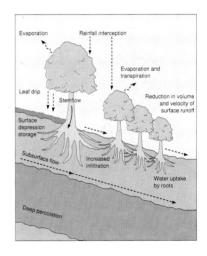

Vegetation helps maintain water balance on site and in the region, and metabolises pollutants in ground water. Avoid planning landscape features which will need irrigation in summer unless provision is being made for the storage and re-use of rainwater or 'grey water'.

A lake, pond or stream on the site usually adds to property value and can be used for fire fighting, but safety is an issue. The size, position, depth and orientation of the body of water are all important to its viability.

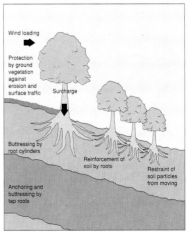

Vegetation helps protect soil and water resources.
Source: CIRIA, 1990

2.8   Maintain Good Soil Condition

The usual measures to protect topsoil and existing vegetation, and to avoid compaction and contamination of the soil, should be written into the specification. Where possible, use vegetation and biodegradable fabrics, rather than engineered structures, to stabilise soil.

The Building Regulations require that "precautions shall be taken to avoid danger to health and safety caused by substances [including contaminants] found on or in the ground to be covered by a building." A contaminant is "any substance which is or could become flammable, explosive, corrosive, toxic or radioactive and any deposits of faecal or animal matter". Sites particularly subject to contamination are listed and signs of contamination are described. Designers are referred to BS 5930: 1981, Code of Practice for Site Investigation, and DD 175: 1988, Code of Practice for the Identification of Potentially Contaminated Land and Site Investigation, for further guidance.

2.9   Plan Sustainable Landscapes

Think of planting in terms of creating a habitat, for animals as well as people, which is part of a larger ecosystem. Using vegetation for shelter or to process carbon dioxide, as described earlier, are just two examples. Specify indigenous species where possible. They will be more robust and less likely to need weedkillers or artificial fertilisers.

If provision is made for recycling organic waste, vegetation can form part of a sustainable cycle within the site boundaries. On suitable sites, food or biomass crops can be grown - a coppice to fuel a stove, an orchard for a school, or vegetable gardens on an apartment site.

Permaculture may be an option on some sites. A form of permaculture which includes the operation and use of buildings can be established on a farm, in a suburban housing development or on a tight urban site. The principles remain the same. The objective is a productive integration of landscape and people to provide food, energy, shelter, and other material and non-material needs in a sustainable way.

2.10   Communicate with Users and Neighbours

The success and continuing viability of the completed project depends heavily on peoples' understanding of sustainable ways of using it. Whether at the scale of the individual building, or of the settlement, there needs to be an educational process which informs the occupants how the systems work. As far as possible, design for methods of operation which are self-explanatory.

The human community forms part of the ecological system and, in this sense, the ecological viability of a project depends on the degree to which local concerns are respected. The needs of the neighbourhood - the social, economic, cultural and organisational context - as well as those of the occupants, should be considered.

Changes to street layout, building scale, uses, landmarks, skylines and familiar materials can damage the character of a place. Nuisances during the construction phase and activity on the site once occupied may disrupt the locality, generating noise, pollution, vibration and the risk of accidents. A project that damages the community in which it sits is not 'sustainable'. It is also less likely to get planning permission or to lead to good public relations.

The way in which the project is initiated, and the conduct of its users after it is built, have a major impact on its image among surrounding residents. It is in the interest of all of the parties, including client, future occupants and community, that some form of community involvement process is used to negotiate the inevitable changes to the context of peoples' lives.

FURTHER READING

- Barton, Hugh, Geoff Davis and Richard Guise. *Sustainable settlements: a guide for planners, designers and developers.* Severnside Research and Consultancy Unit, Faculty of the Built Environment, University of the West of England. Luton, The Local Government Management Board, 1995. Tel. +44 01582 451 166 247 pp. A practical manual offering guidelines, well supported by drawings and diagrams, for design at the scale of town and neighbourhood, with emphasis on residential development.

- *Climate and Site Development.* (BRE Digest 350) Part 2: Influence of Microclimate. Part 3. Improving Microclimate through Design. Watford, UK, Building Research Establishment, 1990.

- Coppin, N. J.. and I. Richards. Use *of Vegetation in Civil Engineering.* (CIRIA, B10). London, Construction Industry Research and Information Association, 1990. 292 pp. £55 Stg.

- ENFO *Fact Sheets, Action Sheets* and *Briefing Sheets* . Three useful series of leaflets covering a range of issues, such as biological diversity, ground water, water supply, tree surveys and composting. Free from ENFO (Environmental Information Service), 17 St. Andrew's Street, Dublin 2. Tel (01) 679 3144

- Environmental Protection Agency. *Advice Notes on Current Practice in the Preparation of Environmental Impact Statements.* Ardcavan, EPA, 1995. 136 pp. £15.00 Includes helpful checklists for assessing the site and the environmental implications of development.

- Lyle, John Tillman. *Regenerative Design for Sustainable Development.* New York, John Wiley, 1994. 338 pp. A practical guide to the theory, design and construction of regenerative systems of energy, water, shelter, food production, waste disposal and other essential functions. Covers scales from region to individual building.

- Lynch, Kevin and Ganz Hack. *Site Planning.* 3rd ed. Cambridge, Mass., MIT Press, 1984. 499 pp. £42.50. Classic text, still relevant.

- McEldowney, S., D. J.. Hordman and S. Waite. *Pollution: Ecology and Biotreatment.* Harlow, Longman, 1993. 322pp. £20.99 Stg. Scientific /engineering treatment of the topic.

Rural Street, Bantry, Co. Cork

MATERIALS

Choosing materials is one of the great pleasures, and trials, of architectural design. With criteria ranging from the aesthetic to the practical, specification has always involved the simultaneous consideration of a wide range of variables and of conflicting performance requirements. Sustainability adds to the complexity. This Sections presents the underlying issues, offers some pointers towards sustainable specification practice, and reviews sources of information which can assist the designer in product selection.

Meander, Foxrock, Co. Dublin, Allen Hope

Processing and manufacturing building products accounts for 70 percent of all energy used in constructing buildings (Energy Related Environmental Issues, BRE.). Attempts to assess in financial terms the overall environmental impact of building materials suggest that in many cases it may be four to five times the market price paid for them (Netherlands Ministry of Housing, Physical Planning and the Environment, 1995). It has been estimated that up to 75 percent of the building materials used in Europe are potentially recyclable. Currently only about five percent is in fact recycled.

If sustainable architecture is the goal, an additional array of selection criteria has to be taken on board, and most designers will need to review their understanding of construction materials and techniques in the light of that objective. This is not easily done. Even if they have an understanding of the underlying principles involved, designers are faced with a frustrating task in assessing the health and environmental characteristics of the materials actually available on the market. There is now a great deal of activity on the part of researchers, product manufacturers and standards agencies, but progress is very uneven.

1 ENVIRONMENTAL IMPACT

Materials have to be thought about in terms of their cycle from 'cradle-to-grave' and their impact at global, local, and immediate level.

1.1 Global Impact

The global energy and pollution implications of using any material depend on its source, on the particular technology used in its extraction and manufacture, and the source of the power used in processing. These vary from country to country, and getting reliable information is difficult. Charts showing approximate levels of embodied energy in generic materials , however, are quite common.

One cannot assume that because a material is 'natural' it is a good choice, and materials which perform well in some circumstances are plainly unsuitable in others. Bentonite Clay, in paperbound building-board form, gels and expands on contact with water to form an impervious layer, but must be kept under pressure by the dead load of basement slabs and retaining walls. It is an excellent example of an ecological building material and provides a very good replacement for petrochemically derived tanking products. But it cannot be used at roof level, even under the weight of a roof garden or a sod roof.

Timber is the classic ecologically-sound and recyclable material, and one much under-used in Ireland. The use of timber for structural purposes calls for as much, if not more, care as steel or reinforced concrete. Specialist engineering advice on fire safety, decay, drying, shrinkage, connections and stress-graded selection is necessary and must be sought from consultants - who tend to prefer the conventional materials. But while most timbers, including tropical hardwoods from sustainably managed plantations, are environmentally sound, specifying timber can have devastating ecological consequences. The use of mahogany from unmanaged plantations is a notable example.

Conversely, aluminium, which is the most energy-intensive of commonly used building materials can, in some circumstances, earn a high eco-rating. If the energy used has a hydroelectric source, then its contribution to greenhouse gas levels is reduced. If it is recycled material, its embodied energy is only five to ten percent that of newly manufactured aluminium. It may also be ecologically appropriate when used in small quantities to improve the longevity and performance of other materials. Its composite use in glazing systems with managed temperate hardwood, to provide tight weathering tolerances, long life and low maintenance, is one example. It should be used strategically, sparingly, and with provision for recycling at the end of its design life.

The issue is not just the absolute environmental impact per kilogram of the material, but also how much of it is used, its contribution to the performance and durability of the building, and its destination at the end of its design life.

Material	kWh/m³
Steel	103000
Aluminium	75600
Single layer roof membrane	47000
Plastics	47000
Glass	23000
Timber (imported softwood)	7540
Clay tiles	1520
Bricks	1462
Plaster/plasterboard	900
Concrete tiles	630
Concrete 1:3:6	600
Local slates	540
Sand and cement render	400
Mineral wool (loose)	230
Timber (local airdried)	110

Embodied energy of common building materials.
Source: Pat Borer, Centre for Alternative Technology, Machynlleth.

Building product life-cycle flow chart

1.2   Local Impact

Local materials should be specified if at all possible. This reduces the energy and pollution costs associated with transport. It also reinforces the vernacular vocabulary, traditional trades, and sense of place, and may generate spin-off social and economic benefits. There can be negative spin-off. Quarrying, for example, causes problems of dust, noise and landscape destruction, so the products of companies which take preventative and restorative action should be favoured.

The local impact in distant places of deforestation, dirty manufacturing processes or exploitative industries represents another ethical issue for the specifier.

1.3   Immediate Impact

Most people are familiar with the 'new car' or 'new building' smell which is produced by the out-gassing of new materials. This may be more serious than it seems.

Data on the health implications of building materials, particularly for construction workers, is improving, and health and safety legislation is encouraging manufacturers to be more informative. However, research into the long-term consequences of low-level emissions from many materials is still in its early stages, with work concentrated on developing standardised test methods and deciding which chemicals most urgently need investigation. Chemicals such as formaldehyde, PCPs, and dieldrins, which are used in some wall coverings, particleboards or dry-rot treatments, may be particularly hazardous for a sleeping or desk-bound person in a confined space. (See also Section B.1: Health and Comfort .)

1.4   Regulations

The only specific reference to sustainability in the Building Regulations is the recommendation in the Technical Guidance Document to Part D that "materials used in building work should, as far as is practicable, be free of CFCs." The Part D requirement that "All works to which regulations apply shall be carried out with the proper materials and in a workmanlike manner" should, in a general way, encourage durable construction.

"Proper materials" means "materials which are fit for the use for which they are intended and for the conditions in which they are to be used, and includes materials which: (a) bear a CE mark in accordance with the provisions of the Construction Products Directive; or (b) comply with an appropriate harmonised standard. . . or (c) comply with an appropriate Irish Standard or Irish Agrément Board Certificate. . .". None of these systems include sustainability among their criteria. The significance of the Construction Products Directive is discussed in Section C. 4: Regulations.

2   SUSTAINABLE SPECIFICATION STRATEGIES

2.1   Define Minimum Performance

Define the minimum performance criteria for the material in terms of aesthetics, use, exposure, design life and maintenance. In a sustainable building the performance criteria will obviously include the contribution which the product will make to the energy performance and health and comfort conditions of the building as a whole. Re-examine standard specification clauses to see if recycled materials could be used without compromising either strength or safety.

2.2   Specify Carefully

Specify materials in a form as close to their natural state as the performance criteria permit. In terms of the complete life cycle of the product, favour:

- Sustainable Source
- Re-Cycled Content
- Low Embodied Energy
- Low Pollution
- Low Toxicity
- No Out-Gassing
- Low Waste Levels
- Greatest Potential for Recycling

2.3   Design for Durability

The tradition of 'firmness' in building is a sound one. In terms of sustainability, design for durability is better than design for recycling, and both are preferable to designed obsolescence.

2.4   Design for Recycling

Favour materials which are themselves recyclable - brick, stone, slate, timber, copper, glass and aluminium, to name a few - and then use them in ways which allows for disassembly for re-use or re-processing. Specifying a mortar which will allow bricks to be salvaged with minimum damage is an obvious example. (see also Section B.11: Wastes)

Environmental benifits derived from substituting recycled materials for virgin resources			
ENVIRONMENTAL BENIFIT	ALUMINIUM %	STEEL %	GLASS %
Reduction of Energy use	90-97	47-74	4-32
Air Pollution	95	85	20
Water Pollution	97	76	-
Water use	-	40	50

Source: Warmer Campaign. Waste Recycling

3   INFORMATION ON SUSTAINABLE PRODUCTS

Practices should consider subscribing to a publication or service which provides on-going information on the sustainability of building products. It is impossible in a book of this kind to give detailed guidance on the use of particular products, or even generic classes of products; and such information would be rapidly outdated. A number of systems and publications which provide information on the embodied energy, ecological, and/or safety performance of building materials are described below. Even these have limitations, and it is clear that a lot of work needs to be done in terms of research, standardisation, and the publication of user-friendly product evaluations.

Any guide to sustainable materials should be used with some caution. It is dangerous to generalise. What is an appropriate choice in one situation may be entirely inappropriate in another. In the choice of materials for sustainable design there are no absolute certainties, and no substitute for independent professional judgement.

The range of sustainable products which are readily available at sensible prices needs to be expanded. Designers, by their specification practices, can influence this. If they consistently seek ecological product information they will encourage movement in the direction of sustainability. A draft questionnaire to accompany product enquires is included in Appendix 3.

Natural and durable materials are sustainable materials, A&D Wejchert.

3.1   Institute for Bau-Biologie

A schedule of materials graded in terms of ecological impact has been developed by Prof. Anton Schneider for the Institute for Bau-biologie and Ecology, Inc. This gives a ranking of generic classes of materials on a simplified scale, and provides a useful starting point for a practice that wants to develop a policy of sustainable specification.

Proprietary building products falling within any of these classes would, of course, vary in their ecological impact. The incorporation of a toxic additive can make an otherwise sustainable material highly undesirable. Timber treated with a preservative containing lindane would be an obvious example.

DCU, Arthur Gibney & Partners.

	Building Material	A	B	C	D	E	F	G	H	I	K	L	M	N	O	P	Q	Grade
1	Timber (solid)	3	3	3	3	3	3	3	3	3	3	3	3	3	3	3	3	3.0
2	Cork	3	3	3	3	3	3	3	3	3	3	3	3	3	3	3	3	3.0
3	Wood particle board	1	1	2	2	3	3	3	3	-	1	2	3	2	0	1	-	1.9
4	Hardboard (Masonite)	1	2	3	2	3	3	3	2	-	1	2	3	2	2	2	-	2.2
5	Veneered block board	2	2	3	2	3	3	3	3	3	1	2	3	2	1	2	-	2.3
6	Woodwool slab (magnesite bonded)	2	2	3	2	3	3	3	3	3	3	3	3	3	3	2	-	2.7
7	Softboard	2	2	3	2	3	3	3	3	3	3	3	3	3	3	3	-	2.7
8	Coconut fibre products	3	2	3	2	3	3	3	3	3	3	3	3	3	3	3	-	2.9
9	Mineral fibres (from slag)	0	0	0	0	0	2	3	3	-	0	0	3	-	-	0	-	0.9
10	Glass fibre (syn. resin bonded)	0	0	0	0	3	1	3	3	-	0	0	3	-	0	0	0	0.9
11	Polystyrene	0	0	0	0	3	0	3	3	0	1	0	3	0	0	0	0	0.8
12	PVC products (hard)	0	0	0	0	3	0	1	2	0	0	0	3	0	0	0	-	0.6
13	Synthetic resin glue	0	0	0	0	3	0	-	-	-	0	0	3	0	0	0	-	0.5
14	Synthetic resin varnish	0	0	0	0	3	0	-	-	-	0	0	-	0	0	0	-	0.3
15	Synthetic woodstains	0	0	0	1	3	3	-	-	-	3	3	-	-	0	0	-	1.3
16	Beewax & products	3	3	3	3	3	3	-	-	-	3	3	-	3	3	3	-	3.0
17	Asphalt & bitumen felt & paper	1	0	1	1	3	3	-	-	0	0	0	-	-	0	0	-	0.8
18	Vapour barrier (foil)	0	0	0	0	3	0	-	-	0	0	0	-	0	0	0	-	0.3
19	Brick products	2	3	3	2	2	3	2	3	3	2	1	3	2	3	3	-	2.5
20	Clay	3	3	3	3	3	3	3	3	3	3	3	2	3	3	3	-	2.9
21	Ceramic products (unglazed)	2	2	2	2	2	3	1	2	-	1	0	3	-	3	3	-	2.0
22	Concrete (reinforced w/steel)	0	0	0	0	1	1	0	1	0	0	0	0	0	3	0	0	0.4
23	Pumice blocks	1	0	1	2	0	2	2	2	-	2	1	0	-	3	0	0	1.1
24	Synthetic gypsum	0	0	0	1	0	-	1	2	0	2	2	3	-	3	1	0	1.1
25	Cement mortar (cement fr. slag)	1	0	2	1	0	3	1	2	-	1	2	0	1	3	1	-	1.3
26	Lime mortar	2	2	3	2	3	3	1	2	-	2	3	2	2	3	2	-	2.3
27	Lime sandstone (bricks)	1	2	3	2	2	3	2	2	-	1	2	1	-	3	2	-	2.0
28	Synthetic resin plaster	0	0	0	1	-	0	1	2	-	0	0	3	0	0	0	-	0.5
29	Linoleum (original)	1	2	3	2	3	3	2	2	3	2	2	3	3	3	3	-	2.5
30	Glass	0	1	1	0	3	0	0	0	-	0	0	3	0	3	3	-	1.0
31	Asbestos cement boards	1	0	0	1	1	-	2	2	0	1	2	3	-	3	1	0	1.2

The Criteria for Evaluation are:

				Ratings
A	Natural occurrence	I	Resistance to microwaves	3 Very desirable
B	Test of time	K	Diffusion/breathing properties	2 Commendable, only minor shortcomings
C	Ecological compatibility	L	Hygroscopicity	1 Doubtful, some shortcomings
D	Energy consumption	M	Moisture content/drying time	0 Undesirable due to considerable
E	Radioactivity	N	Absorption, regeneration	shortcomings
F	Electrical properties	O	Toxic vapours and gases	
G	Thermal properties	P	Smell	
H	Acoustic properties	Q	Skin resistance	

Institute for Bau-Biologie, Ecological assessment of building materials. Source: Helmut Ziehe, Institute for Bau-biologie and Ecology, Inc. Clearwater, Fl, USA.)

3.2 Environmental Preference Method

Developed by Woon/Energie, in the Netherlands, this method reviews the range of materials or components which might be selected for any particular building element. Each of the options has been assessed for its environmental impact over its entire life cycle, from extraction as a raw material to processing of the waste material at the end of the component's life. The results of this assessment are expressed in the form of environmental preference ratings.

Environmental Preference Rating for a Window Frame. Woon / Energie			
Preference 1	**Preference 2**	**Preference 3**	**To be avoided**
Durable wood, unpreserved softwood, carefully detailed	Softwood preserved with boric acid pills	Aluminum, with preserved softwood	PVC-U

The method is easy to use, and the simple ranking of product types allows environmental impact to play a role alongside other criteria, such as price and durability, in the decision making process. *Available as "The Handbook of Sustainable Building" from James & James, Science Publishers, London. £25.00 Stg. Due for publication in early 1996. Tel +44 171 284 3833 Fax +44 171 284 3737.*

3.3 Environmental Resource Guide

Developed by the American Institute of Architects, this provides practical, comparative information on the environmental impacts of building materials, coupled with application reports and case studies. The work is part-funded by the Environmental Protection Agency and an annual updating service is available. Since publication began in 1992 the ratings and reports have become more tentative in response to legal challenges from the industry. The material is nevertheless very useful. *Available from: John Wiley & Sons, Tel. +1 800 225 5945 Fax +1 212 850 6103. $175.00*

3.4 Dublin Institute of Technology Database

The Dublin Institute of Technology has compiled a Database of Embodied Energy for Building Materials. This includes representative values for most materials, with increasing coverage of Irish products. Using a schedule of quantities compiled by the design team's quantity surveyor, DIT can estimate the total embodied energy for a particular design option. Currently this is done manually; software is being developed. *Contact: Ken Beattie, Dublin Institute of Technology, Bolton Street, Dublin 1. Tel (01) 402 3822 Fax (01) 402 3999.*

3.5 Green Building Digest,

A monthly digest providing environmental information for specifiers and purchasers of building materials. Researched and edited by the Ethical Consumers Research Association, it includes 'best buy' rankings for generic materials and environmental analyses of major building product manufacturing companies. Liverpool, ACTAC - The Technical Aid Network, 1995 -. *Available from: ACTAC, 64 Mount Pleasant, Liverpool L3 5SD. Tel. +44 151 708 7607. Annual subscription £60 Stg.*

Office fit-out, Brian Hogan architect.

4   ECO-LABELLING

There are currently over 20 eco-labelling systems in operation world-wide. Some operate within national boundaries only.

There is an EU Eco-Label scheme, but it is intended primarily for retail goods. Criteria for dishwashers, washing machines, paints and varnishes, and single-ended light bulbs have been agreed. Criteria for refrigerators and freezers and for ceramic tiles are in preparation. Furniture, photovoltaic systems, office equipment and household heating systems are under consideration. Attempts to agree criteria for insulation materials collapsed in 1995. It is a voluntary scheme, and in Ireland is administered by the National Standards Authority of Ireland (NSAI).

Two international schemes which appear to have potential for building materials are described below. Both are at the development stage.

4.1   Scientific Certification System (SCS)

A Certified Eco-Profile, presented in bar chart form, is currently being standardised through the International Organisation for Standardisation, Technical Committee on Environmental Management Tools (ISO TC 207). Developed by Scientific Certification Systems, Oakland, California, these 'information disclosure labels' are based on an independent analysis of the entire life-cycle of the product. Providing at-a-glance comparisons of materials, it should lend itself to informed comparative choice. The Certified Eco-Profile label is already in use in the USA. It is open to all product types, but few building materials have yet been assessed. It is the only ISO Type III labelling system operational anywhere.

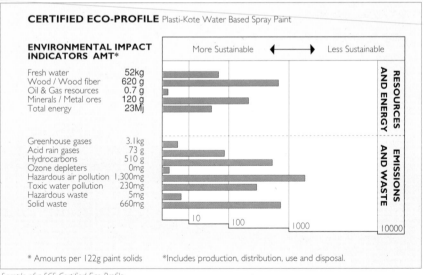

Sample of a SCS Certified Eco-Profile

Children's Court, John Toomey, OPW

4.2   'Swiss Roll' Eco Label

An alternative proposal for eco-labelling is the Swiss Institute of Building Biology Database and Environmental Access System. This circular label is thought by many to provide a more appropriate type of information for building products than the EU Eco-Label. It was endorsed by the First European Eco-Labelling Conference in April 1995.

5   IN-HOUSE DATA BANKS

A practice can establish procedures to build up its own data bank. This will take some time, but will have two advantages. The products or components on file will be ones which fit the project profile of the practice, and they will be products which the practice has established can be reliably sourced to meet project deadlines. A draft questionnaire for use in making enquiries is shown in Appendix 3.

5.1   Gather as much information as possible in a methodical manner. Issue questionnaires. Ask lots of questions, without expecting immediate clear answers from manufacturers. Ask questions in good time.

5.2   Try to establish some basis for comparison. Favour those manufacturers who are making progress toward sustainable methods, and products for which sound information is available.

5.3   If not using a particular material, explain why and invite the supplier to come back when the product is improved.

5.4   Keep clear records. Investigation cut short by deadlines on one project may be continued for another. These records may also serve to support a specification choice in the event of a challenge on compliance.

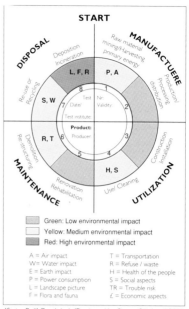

'Swiss Roll' Eco label. (Designed by Bosco Büeler, 1995)

FURTHER READING

- *CFCs in buildings*. (BRE Digest 358). Garston, Building Research Establishment, October 1992 and February 1993

- Construction Industry Research and Information Association (CIRIA). *Environmental Impact of Materials. Volume A: Summary (SP 116)*. London, CIRIA, 1995. £44.00. Fax +44 171 222 1708. Implications and uncertainties of eco-labelling and life-cycle assessment of building materials in general, followed by life-cycle, energy and specification guidance for mineral products; metals; plastics and elastomers; timber and timber products; paints and coatings, adhesives and sealants.

- *European Directory of Energy-Efficient Building 1995 - Components, Materials and Services*. J Owen Lewis and John R Goulding, Editors. London, James & James Science Publishers, 1995. A series of articles on new developments accompanies a European-wide classified listing of companies offering products or services.

- Fox, Avril and Robin Murrell. *Green Design: a Guide to the Environmental Impact of Building Materials*. London, Architecture Design and Technology Press, 1989. 138 pp. Out of print. An easy-to-read A to Z guide.

- *Going Green. The Green Construction Handbook: A Manual for Clients and Construction Professionals*. Research by Ove Arup & Partners. Bristol, JT Design Build Ltd., 1993. Fax +44 1272 290946. Covers the fundamental concepts of 'green' building and provides one-page summaries on generic systems and materials.

- Hall, Keith and Peter Warm. *Greener Building: Products and Services Directory*. 3rd ed. The Green Building Press for the Association for Environment Conscious Building, 1995. Listings are for UK products and companies, but this is more than just a directory. Each product category is preceded by a summary of the issues, with suggestions for sustainable actions.

ENVELOPE

Irish Energy Centre, Dublin, Energy Research Group

In a sustainable building the envelope plays an active role. It collects heat, distributes light, and controls ventilation. It may even generate power. This Section covers the basic principles and reviews some of the less conventional technologies.

In sustainable architecture the link between building performance and the design of the envelope is critical. Any well-built building enclosure is expected to keep out wind, damp and rain, to let in light and air, to conserve heat, and to provide security and privacy. In a sustainable building we may also expect it to collect and store heat, redirect light, control air movement and generate power.

The objective is to use the envelope, insofar as is possible, to take on the functions which in a conventional modern building would be carried out by building services, and to do this with materials and techniques which are themselves environmentally friendly. This is no easy task, but it does present design opportunities for form, light and architectural expression.

A better envelope may sometimes be more expensive to build, but if it improves the balance between heat gain and heat loss , reduces the size of heating plant, eliminates the need for perimeter heating, or cuts fuel bills, its extra cost may be balanced by savings.

The roles the envelope is asked to play in any particular building will depend on the heating, cooling, ventilation and lighting strategies adopted. Is it to be a slow or fast response building ? Is the envelope to be used as a heat store ? Is the primary objective to exploit daylight, to maximise heat gain, or to minimise heat loss ? Are there particular problems of use, site or orientation to be overcome ? (see Sections on Site, Heating, Cooling, Ventilation and Lighting). Choices about materials will be influenced by issues of embodied energy and of health (see Section B.4 : Materials).

I   SUSTAINABLE STRATEGIES

Apart from any ventilation openings they may contain, the opaque areas of walls, floors and roofs are static elements. In the Irish climate their primary purpose, in energy terms, is to conserve heat. For most of the time cooling is not a problem, and there is little need, as there is in hotter climates, to prevent walls from absorbing heat, or to encourage roofs to radiate excess heat to the night sky.

The glazed elements of the building have to be more dynamic. They have a more complex function - solar gain, light transmission, insulation, shading, ventilation, views and communication - and have to respond to short and long term changes in interior and exterior conditions. It is in the area of glazing that some of the most interesting building product developments are taking place.

1.1   Reduce the Task

It makes sense, in the first place, to minimise the scale of the tasks the envelope is asked to fulfil. This will reduce the need for complex or extravagant solutions.

- Site the building where the sun and the light can reach it for solar collection and daylighting.
- Choose or create a sheltered site in the landscape to reduce heat loss through convection and infiltration.
- Create 'buffer spaces' by locating 'cool' rooms on northern or exposed facades, and unheated conservatories or sunspaces on the south. The less the temperature difference between internal and outdoor temperatures, the lower the rate of heat loss through the envelope.

1.2   Minimise Surface to Volume Ratio

The greater the surface area the greater the heat loss, and the greater the quantity of materials that have to be used to construct the envelope. Building form determines surface to volume ratio, so keep it as compact as daylighting and solar collection needs permit.

1.3   Respond to Orientation

The world about the building is not symmetrical. Modify the envelope to respond to the problems and opportunities presented by different facade orientations. Facade design may, in the final analysis, be determined by issues such as context, visual character and coherence, fire safety, and economies of scale. Nevertheless, it often makes sense to specify different materials or forms of construction for different facades. This is particularly true of glazing.

1.4   Keep the Fabric Warm

Unless the building is to be inhabited very intermittently, place insulation as close as practicable to the exterior face of the envelope. This allows the envelope to contribute to the thermal mass of the building, which helps even out interior temperature fluctuations (see Section B.6: Heating). It also raises the radiant temperature of the interior, which helps people feel more comfortable and allows indoor air temperatures to be reduced (see Section B.1: Health and Comfort).

1.5   Design for Durability

Specify for long life and low maintenance to minimise the use of energy and materials over the life of the building.

1.6   Keep it Simple

The paragraphs that follow will describe products and techniques which, put together, can result in a complex and many-layered envelope. Do as much as possible by architectural means before resorting to service installations to fine-tune the indoor environment, but try to keep it simple. Try to ensure that if there are exceptional weather conditions, or the automated or mechanical systems break down, the building can be kept habitable by human intervention.

2   IMPROVING CONVENTIONAL CONSTRUCTION

Using conventional forms of construction, and increasing the thickness and/or thermal resistivity of insulation, it is possible to achieve U-values significantly better than required by Part L of the Building Regulations. Most of the techniques are familiar to designers and builders, but the requirement for good detailing and good workmanship, essential if the values are to be achieved in reality, is sometimes forgotten.

Insulation evenly distributed over all elements generally produces better results than additional insulation applied to only one or two elements. Heat loss calculation methods often instruct the designer to disregard the effects of timber joists or battens, mortar bedding, metal spacers and similar components. The cumulative effect of these discontinuities, combined with the absence of insulation at wall/floor junctions, party walls and window reveals, can be very substantial. In many cases, attention to detailing in these areas, together with careful workmanship, will have greater impact on overall heat loss than simply increasing the thickness of insulation.

Since increasing insulation thickness does not produce a pro-rata reduction in U-value, there comes a point where the economic return on additional insulation for any one element will be virtually nil. The energy cost of manufacturing, transporting and installing it will be greater than the energy savings over the lifetime of the building.

Photovoltaic roof, Roaf House, Oxford. Sue Roaf architect. Photo Credit: Peter Durant.

3   SUPERINSULATION

Superinsulation is an approach rather than a technique. A superinsulated building does not just have more insulation. It is more air-tight, has less thermal bridging, and is built more carefully. Used widely in Canada and in Scandinavian countries, it is often associated with mechanical ventilation, at least during the winter season. (Using air-to-air heat exchangers to transfer heat from exhaust air to supply air reduces the energy cost. Another solution is to use controlled stack-induced natural ventilation.)

As a sustainable strategy, superinsulation has less impact on the architectural character of a building than others. It is less demanding of plan layout, section, orientation, and window design than a passive solar strategy.

The reduction of infiltration by the use of tight-fit components, heavy insulation and weather-stripping has produced well publicised problems for the durability of the building fabric, as well as for interior air quality. Workmanship is critical. But as Nissan and Dutt point out in *The Superinsulated Home Book* : "Superinsulation does not demand an extraordinary standard of work quality. It simply demands quality in an area where it has never before been stressed. A plumbing system must have not have even one leaky pipe; . . . a roofing system must not have even one leak; so an insulation system must not have even one square foot of missed insulation or one hole in the air/vapour barrier." (Nissan and Dutt, 1985)

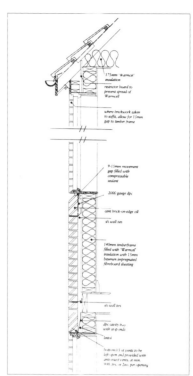

Superinsulated brick-clad breathing wall with U-Value of 0.29 W/m² K. Housing Association Developments, Swansea. PCKO Architects.

4   ROOFS

A well-detailed, well-constructed and durable roof, with good insulation levels, appropriate provision for ventilation, and environment-friendly materials is a sustainable roof. Shingles, mineral slate, and low cement content tiles are among the possibilities for roof coverings. Thatch, being cellular in structure, is an excellent insulator; the U-value of a 45° water reed roof 300 mm thick is 0.35 W/m² K.

An earth roof can provide thermal mass, insulation, and an eco-aesthetic, while helping to conserve landscape on the site. 'Extensive' green roofs have a growing medium 50 mm to 100 mm deep and are generally self sustaining, with hardy plants chosen to tolerate stressful conditions. 'Intensive' green roofs have a growing medium over 200 mm deep and require an irrigation system and intensive maintenance. A green roof system may have many layers from the structural deck up; primer, vapour barrier, a two layer insulation system, a separation film capped by a protection mat, a drainage or retention layer, a filter fleece, growing medium and the vegetation itself (Barton, Davis and Guise, 1995.).

Photovoltaic roofs, in which the photovoltaic panels (see paragraph 1.6) themselves serve as the roofing material, present a very different sustainable solution. In the Sue Roaf House, Oxford, the PV panels are integrated into an aluminium glazing bar system, together with Velux roof lights and solar water-heating panels. The total building cost of the detached six-bedroom house in 1994 was £850/m².

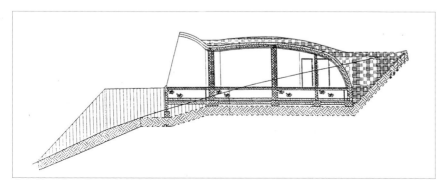

Caglic House, Bevce, Slovenia, by K. Caglic is of earth covered construction.

Grass roof on the Skellig Island Interpretive Centre. Peter & Mary Doyle

5   WALLS

It is in the choice of wall construction that some of the most difficult sustainable design issues arise. The response of products manufacturers to building regulations means that there is now on the market a fairly wide range of materials and components designed to improve U-values and reduce energy consumption. CFC-free insulants are also increasingly available. However, the broader sustainability of the materials or processes used in their manufacture is another matter. The embodied energy in most composite cladding panels, for example, is very high.

Some of the classic 'green' construction techniques, such as rammed earth, or wattle hurdles with clay and lime plaster, are impracticable in ordinary circumstances. A traditional approach with wider application is to bring the roof to meet the ground. In roof construction it is easier to combine high performance with low embodied energy and sustainable materials.

Timber frame construction is an obvious alternative for sustainable building, where fire regulations permit. The 'breathing wall' developed by the Findhorn Foundation is intended to counteract two of the risks of tightly sealed and highly insulated timber frame buildings: interstitial condensation and poor indoor air quality. The permeability of the outer layer of the wall is five times that of the inner layer, so that moisture can pass through the wall without the risk of interstitial condensation. There is doubt as to whether sufficient air passes through the wall to constitute 'air change' for the purposes of ventilation (Crowther and Baker, 1993), but it is possible to construct the walls without the use of materials or preservative treatments involving high embodied energy or hazardous emissions.

Photovoltaic cladding is now becoming feasible. Photovoltaic panels are made of an array of photovoltaic (solar) cells retained between a glass front panel and structural back panel. Integrating PV panels into conventional cladding systems is relatively straightforward. As panel temperature rises, efficiency falls, so the panels are more effective as rainscreen over-cladding, with a ventilated cavity, than as cladding per se. It has been suggested that integrating PV panels into facade or roof structures may add only two percent to the cost of a typical commercial building and provide one third of its electricity requirements (Information Action : Photovoltaics in Buildings). These figures are debated, but payback is improved if the heat removed from the ventilated cavity is captured to contribute to heating the building.

PV Curtain Wall Facade. Pilkington Solar International.

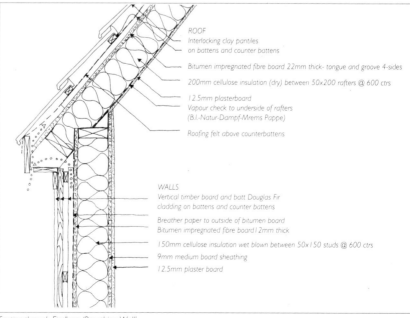

ROOF
Interlocking clay pantiles
on battens and counter battens

Bitumen impregnated fibre board 22mm thick- tongue and groove 4-sides

200mm cellulose insulation (dry) between 50x200 rafters @ 600 ctrs

12.5mm plasterboard
Vapour check to underside of rafters
(B.I.-Natur-Dampf-Mrems Pappe)

Roofing felt above counterbattens

WALLS
Vertical timber board and batt Douglas Fir
cladding on battens and counter battens

Breather paper to outside of bitumen board
Bitumen impregnated fibre board 12mm thick

150mm cellulose insulation wet blown between 50x150 studs @ 600 ctrs
9mm medium board sheathing
12.5mm plaster board

Section through Findhorn 'Breathing Wall'

6   FLOORS

There is evidence that heat losses through ground floors are greater than standard calculations suggest. Draining the ground around foundations can improve performance. Once construction is completed, replacing any materials below ground will be prohibitively costly, if not impossible, so the durability and compatibility of waterproofing, insulants, adhesives, bonding agents, and other materials is important.

Suspended timber floors embody less energy than concrete floors, but a concrete slab, provided that it is not covered with a lightweight finish, can act as a thermal store. A gas-proof membrane to prevent the penetration of radon gas, or sub-floor ventilation to disperse it, should be provided in areas at risk.

7   GLAZING

In a sustainable building the glazing elements are often the most interesting and complex. An urban infill site, for example, may offer no choice whatever in glazing orientation, so that ingenuity in building plan and section, and in the design of the windows, is the only answer. Glazing and window design are the areas in which there have been the greatest technical developments in recent years, with new materials emerging from research laboratories. It is now possible to specify the make-up of a glazing unit to meet the requirements for heat gain, heat conservation, light transmission and light direction, at different latitudes and for different orientations.

Complex, multi-layered windows, which incorporate devices for solar pre-heating, for ventilation or for shading or redirecting light, are now being specified in some projects. In most circumstances, however, simpler solutions can meet requirements.

National Metrology Laboratory, Dublin. Scott Tallon Walker Architects. Transparent insulation in top rows of glazing panels, conceals dropped ceiling behind. (Buschbaum BV).

7.1   Glass

The optical and thermal characteristics of a range of glazing materials. (Figures assembled from product literature of various manufacturers)

Description	Thickness mm (italics denote cavity)	% Direct Radiant Heat Transmission	U-value W/m²K	% Light Transmission
Single clear glass	6	0.83	5.4-5.8	88
Double	*6,12,6*	0.72	2.8-3.0	78
Double with low e coatings	*6,12,6*	0.52	1.7-2.0	74
Triple	6		1.9	69
Triple with two low e coatings	*6,12,6,12,6*	0.45	1.0-1.2	65
Double low e and partially evacuated space	*6,12,6*	0.5-0.75	0.5	74
Double low e and argon	*6,12,6,12,6*	0.5-0.75	1.5	74
Triple 2 low e 2 argon	*6,12,6*	0.45-0.65	0.8	65
Double with reflecting outer pane (antisun float)	*6,12,6*	0.3-0.49	2.7-2.8	36-61
Double with heat absorbing outer pane (suncool float)	*6,12,6*	0.16	2.3-2.6	9-35
Glass block	100	-	2.9	75
Glass block	80	-	3.24	75
Electrically powered sealed insulating glass unit with low e inner pane and argon cavity	*6,12,6*	0.72	1.48 - 0 when operating	72

Transparent insulation and sun control louvred glazing used together at a primary school in Langen, Germany. Remo Gualdi architect.

Okasolar insulating glass with sun control louvres. (Okalux Kapillarglas GmbH)

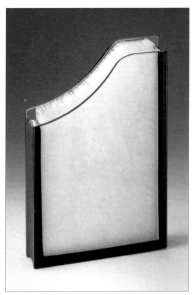

Okalux glass with transparent insulation. (Okalux Kapillarglas GmbH)

7.2   Evacuated Glazing

Double glazed units from which some or all of the air is extracted are being developed. Maintaining the integrity of edge seals over long periods, and preventing the distortion or inward collapse of the glass, are technical problems still to be resolved.

7.3   Chromogenic Glass

Chromogenic glass changes its light absorption and transmission characteristics in response to light changes (photochromic), temperature changes (thermochromic), or to an electrical charge (electrochromic). Control of electrochromic glazing can be incorporated in a building energy management system. Photochromic and electrochromic glasses have reached technical maturity, but material costs are high.

7.4   Transparent Insulation

Sportslink, Santry. Burke-Kennedy Doyle & Partners. Transparent insulation used in rooflighting (Buschbaum BV.). Photo Credit: Barry Mason.

Transparent Insulation Materials (TIM) sandwiched between sheets of glass in a conventional frame can replace traditional windows where light but not vision is required. There are several categories of TIM and light transmission ranges from 45 percent to 80 percent, with a reduction of approximately 8 percent for each sheet of protective glass used. Thermal insulation values are very much better than for glass - 98 mm hexagonal honeycomb polyamid TIM has a light transmission factor of 61 percent, combined with a thermal resistance value five times that of a double glazed window. Costs currently are about three times those of conventional double-glazed windows.

7.5   Window Frames

Since the overall percentage of the area of framing in elevation can be 10 to 20 percent of the opening area, the thermal insulation value of the frame is important.

Frame material	U Value W/m²K
Wood: average thickness >80mm	1.6
Wood: average thickness 50-80mm	2.0
Wood: average thickness <50mm	2.8
Plastic: without metal reinforcement	2.8
Plastic: with metal reinforcement	3.6
Aluminium: with thermal barrier: thermal path length >10mm	3.6
Aluminium: with thermal barrier: thermal path length <10mm	5.0
Aluminium or steel without thermal barrier	7.0

Source: Button and Pye, 1993

7.6   Redirecting Light

Louvres with a specular finish on the upper surfaces of their blades are quite effective in redirecting diffuse light or sunlight into the building. But there are now products, either in advanced development or already on the market, which can 'bend' visible radiation as it passes through the glazing unit.

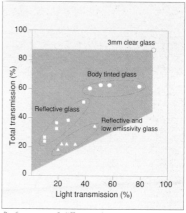

Performance of different glass products showing relationship between light transmission and total solar heat transmission. The shaded area shows the envelope enclosing most practically available architectural glass products. Source: Button and Pye, 1993

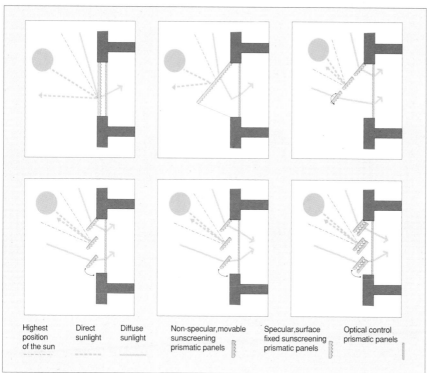

| Highest position of the sun | Direct sunlight | Diffuse sunlight | Non-specular, movable sunscreening prismatic panels | Specular, surface fixed sunscreening prismatic panels | Optical control prismatic panels |

Diagramatic representation of action of prismatic glazing. Source: Siemens.

Translucent sunshield made of prismatic louvres and a venetian blind made of perforated parabolic aluminium louvres (Siemens Product Photograph)

In prismatic glazing the direction of incoming daylight is changed as it passes through an array of triangular wedges, some of which may have specular or silvered surfaces, and whose geometry can be designed for particular conditions. It can keep out unwanted direct sunlight, which causes glare, while admitting diffuse daylight. The light which is admitted can be redirected onto the ceiling, from where it can be reflected farther back into the room. Light coming from different angles can be handled selectively, with assemblies custom-made for site latitude and facade orientation. Normally a prismatic refracting panel consists of two sheets with their prismatic faces facing each other to protect them from dust accumulation. Prismatic sheets can also be used within double-glazed units. While the sheets themselves are inexpensive to manufacture, the overall construction cost is higher than for conventional glazing.

Holographic film can also be designed to handle sunlight coming from well defined angles. High-angle sun on South facades, or low-angle sun on East and West facades, for example, can be either blocked or redirected. Up to four images containing different 'instructions' can be combined in one layer. A view out through the window is retained, but from some viewing angles there is a rainbow effect. Its performance for diffused light is poor, but research is continuing. Costs are not high, but at the moment holographic film is not available in the sizes needed for the building industry.

The Design Centre at Linz, Herzog and Partner. Low slung barrel vault admitting daylight while deflecting solar energy. A glass panel, specially developed with Siemens, forms the outer skin. It is calculated to respond to the seasonal angle of the sun over Linz. Two insulating glass sheets enclose a 16mm thick retro reflecting grid screen coated on one side with aluminium. Only indirect light passes through.

8   SHADING

If sensible glazing ratios are adopted, satisfactory shading is less of a problem. In this climate shading devices are often seen as visually intrusive. If possible they should be kept above eye level where they will not obstruct the view. Simple, occupant responsive systems will generally be better received than automated, high-tech devices.

8.1   Interior or Exterior?

Exterior shades are more effective in reducing heat gains because they intercept and shed, largely by convection, most of the heat in solar radiation. They tend to be more expensive to install and to maintain. They play a major role in the aesthetic character of an elevation.

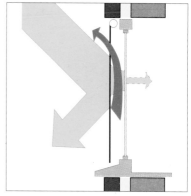

External shading devices.

Interior shades protect a room's occupants against the immediate effects of sunlight and against glare, but once infra-red radiation has penetrated the glazing most of it is trapped inside as heat. If this heat is excessive it must be dissipated by ventilation or by mechanical cooling. Reflective blinds reduce this effect 15 to 20 percent, by reflecting some part of the radiation to the outside. Interior blinds tend to be cheaper, more easily adjustable, and at night can be used to conserve energy and avoid the black-hole effect of windows after dark.

Integral shading installed within a double or triple glazed unit, with mechanical ventilation of the void to the outside, combines the advantages of interior and exterior shades. Heat gains are dissipated to the outside, but the shades are protected from the severity of the outdoor climate. In this context there is considerable overlap between 'shading devices' and the 'light-directing' products described above.

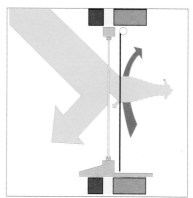

Internal shading devices.

8.2   Fixed or Adjustable?

Fixed horizontal overhangs exclude high-angle sunlight, but reduce daylight penetration and are of limited usefulness for East and West orientations. Continuous overhangs provide much more shade than those which extend across the width of the window only.

Low-angle direct sunlight is more difficult to screen. Fixed vertical fins, if they are to be really effective, exclude a great deal of daylight and obstruct the view. Steel mesh sunscreens are almost 'transparent' but they too reduce the amount of daylight penetrating the windows.

Adjustable shades avoid some of these problems. Retractable awnings, adjustable exterior blades, curtains, roller blinds or venetian blinds can be left open for much of the time and closed only when the sun-angle demands it. On east or west-facing facades, horizontal louvres need to be almost completely closed to block sunlight, but vertical louvres can be left partially open to admit reflected or diffused light from the north, while still blocking sunlight. In Ireland's climate, adjustment will be frequent and in non-domestic buildings cannot always be left to the occupants. Fully automated systems, which respond to changes in sun angle, temperature and/or light levels, may be necessary, particularly for exterior systems.

Insulated roller shutter and box.

9 SHUTTERS

Insulating shutters which are closed after dark can be useful in reducing heat loss. Creating a well-sealed air gap between shutters and glazing increases effectiveness, but can be difficult to achieve. External shutters are preferable; internal shutters may lead to condensation on the glass during cold conditions, or, if left closed while the sun shines, set up thermal stresses which cause the glass to break. However, managing the operation of external shutters is not easy; in cold weather the occupants are unlikely to open windows to close the shutters. A louvred shutter operated from the inside can overcome this problem, but it may also interfere with light penetration during the day.

10 VENTS

Where opening lights in windows present problems, operable vents, whether separate or integrated in a window assembly, are worth considering. With air flow control, insect and dust screens, or acoustic baffles, they can provide a relatively inexpensive solution where noise or air pollution create difficult site conditions.

FURTHER READING

- Button, David and Brian Pye, Editors. *Glass in Building: a Guide to Modern Architectural Glass Performance.* Oxford, Butterworth Architecture for Pilkington Glass Ltd., 1993. 372 pp. £40 Stg. Comprehensive coverage of lighting, thermal, acoustic and mechanical functions of glazing.

- Compagno, Andrea. *Intelligent Glass Facades: Material, Practice, Design.* Basel, Birkhauser Verlag, 1995. 128 pp. £44 Stg. Covers a wide range of working examples by Ritchie, Grimshaw, Nouvel and others. Aimed at architects, structural and services engineers.

- Nisson, J. D. Ned and Guatam Dutt. *The Superinsulated Home Book.* John Wiley & Sons, 1985. out of print.

- Talbott, John L. *Simply Build Green: A Technical Guide to the Ecological Houses at the Findhorn Foundation.* Findhorn, Findhorn Foundation Development Wing, 1993. 200 pp. Out of print.

- UK. Department of the Environment. Energy Efficiency Office. *Energy Efficiency in New Housing: Detailing for Designers and Building Professionals. Good Practice Guides Nos. 93 - 97.* London, HMSO, 1993-95. Guide 93 Key detailing principles; Guide 94 Ground floors; Guide 95 External cavity walls; Guide 96 Windows and external doors; Guide 97 Pitched roofs. A useful series of 8 - 29 page publications, well-illustrated, highlighting areas of risk, with advice on specification and buildability.

HEATING

The Point Depot, Dublin, Shay Cleary Architects.

In Ireland's mild climate the sun can make a substantial contribution to heating. Passive solar space heating is the strategy that has most to offer under Irish conditions. Active solar systems can contribute to space and water heating, but payback is more problematic. Both are covered in this Section, which also includes some advice on increasing the efficiency and minimising the environmental impact of conventional heating systems.

An estimated 67 percent of the primary energy consumed by services in Irish buildings is used for space heating and cooling. Another 12 percent is used for service water heating. In residential buildings the figure for space and water heating combined is 94 percent. In existing buildings with poor comfort standards higher levels of energy efficiency may be partially absorbed in improved comfort levels. In general, however, improvements in energy-efficiency will translate into reduced energy consumption. For most new buildings a 20 percent reduction in heating bills is feasible at negligible capital cost. Significantly larger savings can be achieved if a comprehensive low-energy design strategy is adopted.

For any building there are five potential sources of heat: internal gains (from lighting, occupants and equipment); solar gains; heat from other renewable sources (wind or hydro-power, for example); heat generated by fossil fuels; or heat recovered (from any source) within the building.

All buildings obtain some heat from the sun but, with intelligent design, solar energy can make a sizeable contribution towards meeting heating demand. Good insulation and low levels of infiltration shorten the heating season at each end, so that a greater proportion of the heating season falls within the period when solar radiation is at low levels. Nevertheless, even in a well-insulated building, solar gain combined with internal gains from occupants and their equipment can have a significant impact on heating demand.

Passive solar space heating is the strategy that has most to offer under Irish conditions. It depends on the form and fabric of the building and, at the simplest levels, need involve no additional expenditure whatever. Active solar systems can contribute to space and water heating, but the higher installation costs combined with current low energy prices make payback periods less attractive.

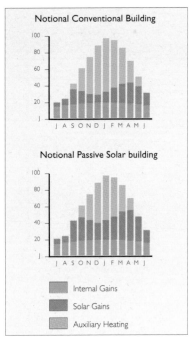

Notional Conventional Building

100
80
60
40
20

J A S O N D J F M A M J

Notional Passive Solar building

100
80
60
40
20

J A S O N D J F M A M J

■ Internal Gains

■ Solar Gains

□ Auxiliary Heating

Contributions of internal gains, solar gains and auxiliary heating in a conventional building and a passive solar building.

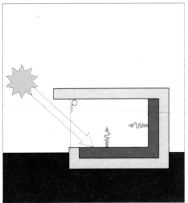

Typical direct gain passive solar dwelling.

The aim of passive solar design is not to maximise solar gain, but to minimise consumption of fossil-fuel based energies. Arriving at the optimum solution for a particular brief and a particular site involves considering all of the issues in relation to each other.

A Direct Gain system, based on the 'greenhouse effect', is the most useful passive solar collection strategy for Ireland's climate. It is the simplest solar collection technique, and the easiest to build, depending largely on conventional construction components and methods. Mass Walls, Trombe Walls, or Water Walls are less effective at Irish latitudes because they demand high levels of sunshine during the heating season. If the price of transparent insulation were to fall significantly, Mass Walls could become viable.

In a direct gain system, short-wave solar radiation is collected through glazing, absorbed by the walls, floors and other solid elements, then re-emitted into rooms as long wave radiation which the glazing prevents from leaving the building. Passive solar collection through opaque walls or roofs is not practicable in Ireland. More heat will be lost through an uninsulated south-facing wall or roof than can ever be collected from the sun, while solar gain through conventionally insulated walls and roofs would, of course, be negligible.

Well-insulated buildings are vulnerable to overheating in summer. In a passive solar building good window design, appropriate shading, natural cooling techniques and sensible control systems can all be exploited to maintain a balance.

Limerick RTC, Limerick, Murray O'Laoire

I   DESIGNING A DIRECT GAIN SYSTEM

It is assumed that by this stage the site and its microclimate will have been evaluated, particularly in relation to slope, orientation and any obstructions to light, and that the availability of solar radiation on the site has been established (see Sections B.2: Climate, and B.3: Site)

It is possible to evaluate decisions step-by-step through the design process, and techniques for doing so will be suggested at each stage. However, procedures for evaluating overall performance are more important, and these are discussed in paragraph 1.5 of this Section.

The four elements of any solar heating system are Collection, Conservation, Storage and Distribution.

1.1   Solar Collection

The critical factors for solar collection are the orientation and slope of glazing, the glazing ratio, and the characteristics of the glazing materials. It is essential, naturally, that any glazing intended to function as a solar collector is not overshadowed by vegetation or by nearby buildings, particularly during the hours around solar noon. Winter solar noon occurs at 12.25 in the East and 12.40 in the West of the country.

1.1.1   Orientation:

While a south-facing surface receives more solar radiation in winter than any other, the radiation on south-east and south-west facing surfaces between November and March is over 80 percent of that for true South. This gives some flexibility in selecting the orientation of a building and of its glazing.

East or west facing glazing is often problematic in non-domestic buildings. Heat gains from low-angle morning and evening sun will be considerable, but much of it will occur at the ends of, or outside, the heating season. Provided that steps are taken to deal with glare, glazing on the east facade can provide useful gains in the early hours of the day, but west-facing glazing will be collecting radiation at a time when interior temperatures may be at their peak. During the summer, east and west facing glazing may receive more solar radiation than south facing windows do, and overheating is likely. Screening low-angle sun without excluding daylight is difficult. Net solar gain (solar gain less window heat loss) for double-glazed windows facing North, East or West, and South are shown here. North-facing surfaces receive no direct radiation during the heating season.

House at Doolin, Co. Clare, Grafton Architects. North and south facing facades.

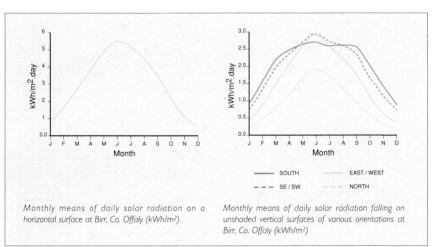

Monthly means of daily solar radiation on a horizontal surface at Birr, Co. Offaly (kWh/m²).

Monthly means of daily solar radiation falling on unshaded vertical surfaces of various orientations at Birr, Co. Offaly (kWh/m²)

1.1.2   Slope

Vertical glazing is generally preferable. Vertical glazing facing more-or-less south will collect a high proportion of low-angle winter sun, which is beneficial, and somewhat less of high-angle summer sun, which is usually not.

Sloped or horizontal glazing tends to collect more high-angle sun, less low-angle sun, and loses more heat by radiation in winter and at night. This results in less heat gain in winter, overheating in the summer and on warm winter days; and heat losses when they are least desirable. However, sloped glazing can be used effectively in properly designed atria and sunspaces.

1.1.3   Glazing Ratio

The glazing ratios quoted in this section should be used as a starting point only, and modified in the light of subsequent evaluation during the design process.

A typical passive solar domestic building has relatively large windows on the south-facing facade. Windows facing north are kept as small as daylighting needs allow, so as to minimise heat losses. For Irish conditions a glazing area of approximately 20 percent of floor area is reasonable, 60 percent to 70 percent of which should be on the south facade. Unless site constraints are particularly difficult, it is almost always possible to allocate suitable spaces and uses to the north-facing, small-windowed side of the house.

In non-domestic buildings it is much less likely that all of the spaces which need high levels of daylight can be accommodated on south-facing facades. However, in large non-domestic buildings the surface-to-volume ratio tends to reduce, fabric losses to decrease, and occupation density and internal gains to increase. If the building is in use only during the day, when air temperatures and solar gains are high, internal gains may meet heating demand for much of the time, and the energy value of the daylight received through glazing, even on a north-facing facade, may compensate for the heat losses through it.

For buildings occupied only during office hours, the glazing ratios (for double glazing) required to minimise total annual energy consumption (heating + cooling + lighting) under Irish climate conditions might be approximately as follows:

South facing	25 - 35%
East/West facing	20 - 30%
North facing	20 - 30 %

Ratios are heavily dependent on the particular building type and site conditions which, of course, vary widely. For buildings which are also used after dark the ratios will be lower, unless effective window insulation - insulated shutters, for example- is installed. The surprisingly high ratios for East and West facing facades results from the fact that the overheating which occurs at some times is balanced, on an annual basis, by useful solar gains at other times. If comfort conditions inside the building are to be maintained, adjustable shading will be essential.

The LT Method (see Section C.1: Tools for Design and Evaluation), which is designed to help a design team evaluate the strategic implications of early proposals for building form and glazing ratios, can be helpful at this stage.

Requirement L1 of the Building Regulations has implications for glazing ratios. Of the three methods for calculating overall heat loss given in the *Technical Guidance Document* to Part L, only the "Net Heat Loss Method" takes solar gain and orientation into account, and it is considered suitable for housing only. However, nothing in the *Technical Guidance Document*, nor in the regulations themselves, precludes the use of other calculation methods provided that they can show that the building will perform at least as well as if designed in accordance with the methods given in the *Document*. The issue is discussed further in paragraph 1.5 of this Section.

1.1.4   Characteristics of Glazing Materials

The amount of solar radiation collected by any window is affected by the type of glazing specified.

The solar transmission and insulation characteristics of a range of glazing types is given in Section 5: Envelope

1.1.5   Estimating Solar Gain:

Net solar gain (raw solar gain less window heat loss) through windows in a given building can be calculated using the manual procedure shown in Appendix 4, but this can be a time consuming exercise. Software tools such as .PASSPORT (see Section C.1) can predict both solar and internal gains for residential buildings. Alternatively, the design team may choose to carry out a broader assessment of proposals (see paragraph 1.5).

Not all solar gain is useful in reducing the heating load. Some may contribute to overheating, particularly on sunny days near the beginning and end of the heating season; and some may be provided at times when the building is unoccupied. Useful solar gains do not increase linearly with window size, because there is proportionately more gain during the summer, when it is not needed, and proportionately more heat loss during cold weather. The fraction of total solar gain over a given period which actually contributes to the target comfort levels is referred to as the 'utilisation factor'. In mid-winter its value will be in the region 80 - 100 percent, falling towards zero at the beginning and end of the heating season. Averaged over the whole heating season, useful solar gain will be somewhat less than net solar gain.

Estimated net solar gain of unobstructed clear south-facing windows at Birr, Co. Offaly. Transmission losses for a well insulated wall are shown for comparison (Assumed internal temperature = 18°C).

1.2   HEAT CONSERVATION

Once collected, useful solar gain must be retained within the building, and the usual principles of heat conservation apply:

- Low surface to volume ratio
- Reduction of the surface area facing north, or exposed to prevailing winds
- Insulation of building envelope
- Control of ventilation and infiltration
- Use of draught lobbies
- Thermal zoning of interior spaces
- Location of spaces with lower heat requirements ('buffer spaces') on cold side of building

If south-facing glazed areas are to be larger than the size required for daylighting, so as to increase solar gain, their U-value must be improved. But lower U-values in glazing are usually associated with some reduction in light transmittance. On the other hand, improving the U-value of glazing will raise the mean radiant temperature in a space, and so reduce the air temperature required for comfort. A balance has to be struck.

An alternative approach is to use glazed areas no larger than those required for daylighting, but to install very high levels of insulation, while taking particular care to eliminate cold bridges and minimise infiltration losses. In such a building the solar gains from conventionally sized windows should meet a significant proportion of the low heating demand.

The object of the exercise, as noted earlier, is not to maximise solar gain but to minimise the consumption of fossil-fuel based energy.

1.2.1 Evaluating Thermal Balance

Setting total raw solar gain through glazing against total building fabric heat loss will give an approximate indication of thermal balance, but takes no account of daylighting or of ventilation losses. The LT Method (see Section C.1) can be used to give a rough indication of the glazing ratios for roofs and facades which will produce the minimum total energy consumption for heating, lighting and cooling combined. The software programs commonly used by services engineers can also quickly provide useful feedback at this stage.

1.3 HEAT STORAGE

Ideally all surplus solar gain in a space should be transferred to other spaces that need it, or stored for later use. Both processes present practical problems which may limit the extent to which this can be achieved.

Well positioned thermal mass can absorb and store solar energy during the day, releasing it slowly during the night. It will absorb heat generated by people, lighting, and equipment as well as by the sun, so has the additional advantage of moderating temperature swings and reducing the risk of overheating.

Thermal mass can be provided by walls, floors or other solid elements within the building. The heat storage capacity of ordinary building materials depends mainly on their density. For storage and release on a 24 hour cycle the effective thickness of masonry is 60 - 120 mm, so for most buildings there is no advantage in providing exceptionally thick walls or floors for thermal storage purposes.

However, if the building structure is to be used as a thermal store, then raised floors and/or suspended ceilings should be avoided. This may not be critical in small buildings, where services can be run around the perimeter. In deeper buildings they may have to be run on the surface, or in channels or voids within the structure. Low density finishes also, such as timber or carpeting, act as insulating layers and inhibit heat absorption. Dark coloured finishes increase absorption of short-wave radiation by sufaces directly in the sun. Colour has no significant effect on the absorption of heat re-radiated from other surfaces, so ceilings, window walls and any other surfaces which receive no direct radiation can be pale in colour.

Masonry walls which are externally insulated will contribute to the thermal mass of the building. If they are internally insulated, they will not. Timber frame or industrial type sandwich-panel systems provide negligible thermal mass. A high thermal mass strategy is not always appropriate. In an intermittently used building it may actually increase energy consumption by requiring long preheating periods.

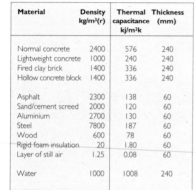

Material	Density kg/m³(r)	Thermal capacitance kj/m²k	Thickness (mm)
Normal concrete	2400	576	240
Lightweight concrete	1000	240	240
Fired clay brick	1400	336	240
Hollow concrete block	1400	336	240
Asphalt	2300	138	60
Sand/cement screed	2000	120	60
Aluminium	2700	130	60
Steel	7800	187	60
Wood	600	78	60
Rigid foam insulation	20	1.80	60
Layer of still air	1.25	0.08	60
Water	1000	1008	240

Densities and thermal capacitance of building materials. Source, Goulding, 1992

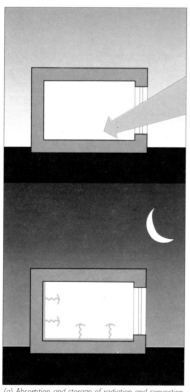

(a) Absorption and storage of radiation and convection and (b) Release of heat stored in thermal mass

1.4   HEAT DISTRIBUTION

After a time lag, some of the heat generated by solar gains will find its way through the building by conduction, convection and radiation. Natural thermo-circulation, caused by hot air rising, can be used to distribute heat generated by direct solar gain in one zone to another cooler zone. This demands judicious planning and is often made difficult by requirements for acoustic privacy or fire compartmentation. There must be provision for closing off this circulation at night or during cloudy periods; otherwise a reverse loop may occur and cause unwanted cooling.

Where natural air movement within the building is insufficient or unhelpful, fans can be used to assist its flow. Routing warm air from a sunspace to north-facing rooms, or from an attic space to the ground floor, are common examples. This is pointless, of course, if the energy used to drive the fan exceeds the energy saved on heating.

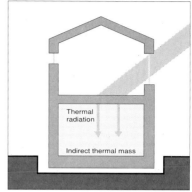

Heat distribution by conduction and thermal radiation

1.5   EVALUATING PASSIVE SOLAR DESIGN PROPOSALS

As is clear from this description, heating/cooling design has to be carried on in parallel with daylighting design (see Section B.9: Lighting). As was mentioned earlier, the LT Method (see Section C.1), which considers heating, lighting and cooling together, can be very useful for evaluating proposals at the sketch design stage.

As the design develops, firmer information about solar gains and about internal gains - due to occupants, activities, processes, equipment, and artificial lighting - will become available, and can be fed into the calculations.

Heat distribution by natural thermo-circulation

Evaluation at this stage can still be done manually. A manual procedure for calculating space heating requirements in a building is given in Appendix 5. It takes into account solar gain, internal gains, fabric heat loss and ventilation heat loss. Alternatively, software programmes such as those listed in Section C.1 can be used. Daylighting will have to be assessed in parallel.

Typical figures for internal gains in a three bedroom house

	kWh/day
Occupants	4.0
Lighting	1.5
Appliances and Cooking	6.5
Hot water	3.0
Total	15.0

Nominal figures for internal gains in an office building

People	11 W/m² (sensible + latent heat, assuming 1 person per 10m²)
Lighting	10 - 12 W/m² (assuming energy-efficient lighting)
Computers	100 - 140 W each (including CPU)
General equipment	10W/m² (in single person offices)
	6 W/m² (in open plan offices)

Producing a building which performs at least as well as required by the Building Regulations should present no difficulty if the design team has been pursuing sustainable strategies. If the estimated annual demand for space heating in the building (using any suitable calculation method) is less than the estimated annual demand of a similar "reference" building (calculated by the 'Overall Heat Loss Method' in the Technical Guidance Document to Part L), the building will perform better than required by the Regulations. To check this the following procedure can be used.

• Choose a design temperature and calculate the total annual space heating energy demand for your building. (Degree days for some locations are given in Appendix 7. For other locations contact the Meteorological Service.)

- Sketch a reference building of similar floor area, profile, and use.
- Calculate (from TGD Table I, and examples I, B2 or B3, appendix B) the maximum average acceptable U value for the reference building.
- Calculate the total heat loss (roof, walls, exposed floors, windows) per degree temperature difference of the reference building.
- Calculate the total annual space heating energy demand for the reference building. (Use the same design temperature and the same degree days as you used for your building.)
- Check this figure against the total annual space heating demand for your building.

This procedure, of course, ignores any reductions in overall energy consumption gained by optimising the balance between natural and artificial heating, lighting and ventilation.

It is expected that revisions to the Technical Guidance Document to Part L will include a procedure for calculating an energy rating for dwellings, which will take solar gain and ventilation into account.

2   SUNSPACES AND ATRIA

Atria and sunspaces can both can make a contribution to a passive solar design strategy.

2.1   Sunspaces:

During the heating season a south-facing sunspace or conservatory will collect solar energy and, by acting as a buffer space, reduce heat losses. It can also be used to preheat ventilation air. This can be a substantial benefit. Raising the air temperature from 4°C (outdoor temperature) to 12°C, for example, can halve the ventilation heat load. It is essential that the sunspace can be closed off from heated areas of the building when necessary. The low radiant temperatures of the large glazed surfaces will make the sunspace too cold to function as a living space except in mild or sunny weather, but if it is artificially heated heat losses through the glazing will far outweigh any solar gains.

The Building Regulations make no specific provisions for the conservation of fuel and energy in unheated ancillary areas such as conservatories and sunspaces.

2.2   Atria

Atria can provide useful and enjoyable space for climate-tolerant activities such as circulation or window-shopping, while reducing overall energy consumption. This requires careful analysis of the interactions between the heating, ventilation, cooling and lighting needs of both atrium and adjacent spaces. Many atria are poorly designed and increase instead of decreasing heating costs.

An atrium, like a sunspace, can reduce heating loads by collecting solar energy, preheating ventilation air and acting as a buffer between heated spaces and the external environment. The reduction in transmission heat loss through the walls adjoining the atrium means that their glazing ratios can be increased. This raises daylight levels in the building proper and reduces lighting energy consumption. Since annual lighting costs in large buildings often outweigh heating costs, this can result in significant savings. (Daylighting aspects of atria are dealt with in Section B.9: Lighting)

Sunspace at The Green Building, Dublin, Murray O'Laoire

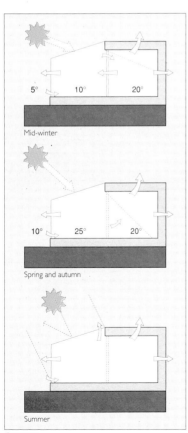

5°   10°   20°

Mid-winter

10°   25°   20°

Spring and autumn

Summer

Sunspace

The atrium itself should not be heated. Solar gains, transmission heat losses through the separating walls and exhaust ventilation air from the building can keep its temperature in a range well above outdoor temperatures during cold weather.

Overheating of the atrium in summer can be prevented by ventilation and by shading. If cross ventilation and/or the stack effect are not sufficient, fans can be used to boost ventilation under extreme conditions. Shading devices should be adjustable, to accommodate winter and summer conditions, and can be designed to act as insulation at night. High sky luminances in summer can provide good daylight penetration of adjacent spaces even when the atrium is shaded. In winter, when sky luminances are lower, overheating is less likely and the shades can be retracted.

When planning ventilation strategies for an atrium, consult the fire authorities at an early stage.

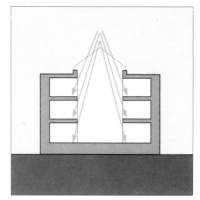

Atrium section

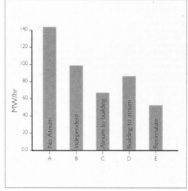

Annual heating energy consumption for a building with an atrium:
A: No atrium.
B: Atrium present, but no ventilation coupling with the building.
C: Ventilation pre-heating.
D: Ventilating air expelled into atrium, raising its temperature.
E: Recirculation of air between building and atrium.
Source: Baker, 1995

The Green Building, Dublin, Murray O'Laoire

3   ACTIVE SOLAR SPACE HEATING

Because heavy cloud cover in winter tends to be associated with relatively mild air temperatures, and very low temperatures generally coincide with clear skies, the potential for active solar space heating in Ireland is greater than might be imagined.

A whole-house system currently being marketed in Ireland incorporates 'triple-glazed' air-heating solar collectors, an air handling unit, and ducted warm air/ventilation supply. Heat is reclaimed from return air by a heat exchange unit. During the summer the system provides the bulk of hot water heating. An electronic control system manages the installation, and a conventional boiler provides back-up in cloudy winter weather. Thermal mass plays a significant role; ground, first and attic floors are hollow concrete slab. Keeping building fabric and infiltration heat losses to a minimum is critical. Combined space and water heating costs for a three-bedroom semi-detached house are claimed to be about £75 per year.

Installation costs are higher than for a conventional heating system. The system is designed for new build (the solar collectors form an integrated part of the roof structure), but if a building already has a warm-air heating system retrofitting may be an option *Contact: Energy Resources International Ltd., 1 Cookstown Square, Cookstown Industrial Estate, Dublin 24. Tel (01) 451 6516 Fax (01) 451 6517*

4   SOLAR WATER HEATING

In an active solar water heating system solar energy is absorbed by the collector, used to heat a heat-transfer fluid, then transferred through a heat exchanger to water in a hot-water storage vessel.

The collector is usually, but not necessarily, mounted on the roof. At Ireland's latitude the optimum orientation for maximum annual hot water production is south facing, and the optimum inclination angle 30° to 40°. But an orientation of anywhere between south-east and south-west, and an inclination of anywhere between 10° and 60°, will give a performance reasonably close to the optimum. Optimal inclination for water heating is shallower than for space heating because of year-round application.

Evacuated tube collectors are more efficient and can attain higher temperatures than flat plate collectors, though they tend to be more expensive, and some use CFCs as a heat transfer fluid. Flat-plate collectors are generally suited to low-temperature applications such as domestic hot water; evacuated tube collectors (with 'ozone-friendly' heat transfer fluids) are more appropriate for higher temperature applications.

As a rule of thumb in sizing domestic systems, there should be about $1m^2$ of flat-plate collector area ($0.7m^2$ for evacuated tube collectors) for each occupant. A correctly sized system can provide about 80-90 percent of hot water energy needs in summer, perhaps 15-20 percent in winter, with an annual average (solar fraction) of about 50 percent . The British Standards Institution *Designer's Manual for the Energy Efficient Refurbishment of Housing* puts the payback period at five to eight years at current energy prices .

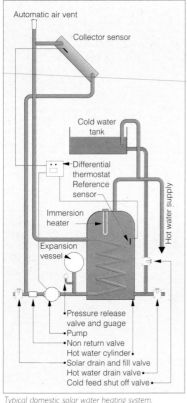

Typical domestic solar water heating system.

Mean annual solar irradiation on south-facing surfaces at various locations (kWh/m²).			
Location	Inclination to horizontal		
	0°	30°	60°
Belfast	916	1040	971
Birr	1010	1150	1077
Valentia	1038	1161	1066

In a non-domestic building with relatively uniform demand for hot water throughout the year a flat-plate collector area of 1m² for each 45 litres of daily hot water demand (at 60° storage temperature) should provide approximately 50 percent of the annual hot water demand. However, demand patterns and other factors affect system sizing and expert advice should be sought. *Contact: Dr. Sean McCarthy, Hyperion, Main Street, Watergrasshill, Co. Cork. Tel (021) 889461 Fax (01) 889 465 or Energy Research Group, School of Architecture, University College Dublin, Richview, Clonskeagh, Dublin 14. Tel (01) 269 2750 Fax (01) 283 8908.*

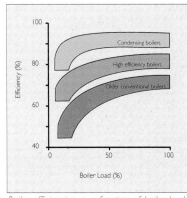

Typical solar contribution to hot water demand.

5 HEAT PUMPS

A heat pump can be used to extract usable heat from a low temperature source such as the earth, outdoor air, or water. These are, of course, renewable resources, but, because the pump uses electricity for compression and circulation, the financial and primary energy implications need careful assessment

6 FOSSIL-FUEL HEATING SYSTEMS

It is possible, where normal budget constraints do not apply, to design a 'zero energy' building for the Irish climate but, in practice, most buildings will need some conventional heating. However, in a passive solar building, fuel consumption should be substantially reduced and some reduction in plant size should be possible.

6.1 Fuels and Appliances

When choosing fuels for conventional heating systems consider the pollution produced by burning the fuel, and the efficiency with which it can be used in available heating equipment. The energy and pollution inherent in processing and transport ought also to be a factor, but information is not readily available.

The Building Regulations contain no specific requirements as to the efficiency of heating appliances. All-electric heating, which is questionable in environmental terms, is permitted.

Boiler efficiencies as a function of boiler load. (BRECSU Guide for installation of condensing boilers in economical buildings. 'Good Practice Guide 16')

Typical emission factors for fuels (based on gross calorific value)		
Fuel	CO_2	SO_2
	(kg/kWh)	(g/kWh)
Gas	0.18	0
LPG	0.22	0
Gas Oil	0.25	0.5
Fuel Oil	0.26	5
Coal	0.30-0.35	2 - 3
Peat	0.36	1
Electricity	0.80	8

6.2   CONTROLS

Typical heating appliance efficiencies	
Open fire	15 - 30%
Oil-fired boiler	55 - 70%
Gas fired boiler	65 - 75%
Gas room heater	65 - 75%
Condensing boiler	80 - 90%
Electric room heater	100% nominal, but only 35% if account is taken of the primary energy consumed in electricity generation.

The heating system must be fitted with controls to ensure that heat is provided only when it is needed, and then as efficiently as possible. The Building Regulations give some guidance on controls for space heating and hot water supply, but these go no further than generally accepted good practice. The room thermostats, thermostatic radiator valves, timers, optimising controls, external temperature sensors (weather compensation controls) and boiler controls recommended are all familiar to experienced designers.

The effectiveness of any system can be compromised by inappropriate occupant behaviour, and it is particularly important in passive solar buildings that users are well informed about how the building operates. If, for example, people open windows, instead of turning down radiators, at times of high solar gain in mid-winter, the building's energy performance will not be as good as predicted. The need for user co-operation can be reduced by installing automatic controls, but at higher cost and also with the risk of equipment failure. The likely level of user co-operation must be assessed and control systems designed accordingly.

A building energy management system (BEMS) can be a powerful tool for optimising energy use and equipment maintenance schedules. However, if its full potential is to be realised, building managers must be given adequate training, and the time to monitor the information which the BEMS provides and to act on it. Many existing systems are under-exploited, with the result that opportunities for energy and cost savings are lost. (Control systems in general are discussed in Section B.13: Ensuring Good Performance.)

6.3   COMBINED HEAT AND POWER

In a conventional electricity generation plant a large amount of waste heat is released into the atmosphere, resulting in an overall efficiency of only 30 to 35 percent. In a combined heat and power (CHP) plant, most of this heat is reclaimed for use in space, water or process heating. Efficiencies of up to 95 percent are achievable, and CO_2 production is reduced.

Small CHP units - 20kW to 1 MW - are now available at reasonable cost. If a building or group of buildings has a reasonably large demand for both heat and electricity, the installation of a CHP plant is well worth considering. Hotels and hospitals, for example, are likely candidates. The unit, which may be gas or oil-fired, is usually installed in the boiler room and connected to the building's heating and electrical supply systems. Electricity not used in the building can, in some circumstances, be fed to the ESB grid. *Contact: Michael Brown, European Association for the Promotion of Cogeneration (COGEN Europe), Brussels. Tel +32 2 772 8290 Fax +32 2 772 5044, or Bill Quinn, Irish Energy Centre, Glasnevin, Dublin 9. Tel (01) 836 9080 Fax (01) 837 2848.*

6.4   DISTRICT HEATING

Heat is generated at a central location, either as a by-product of industrial processes, or specifically for heating purposes. It is then transferred through insulated hot water pipes to other buildings in the area, where it is metered and billed to consumers.

At this scale it is economic to install flue-gas cleaning equipment and additional controls, which will improve efficiency and reduce emissions. This means that a wide range of fuels can be used; either the cheapest available at any particular time, or dirty fuels - including polluting, but sustainable, materials such as wood or straw or waste.

Installing a district heating scheme in an existing housing estate or office park would in most cases be uneconomic. In new estates it may be worth considering, particularly if there is an existing heat source nearby. District heating tends to be most effective in mixed use estates, where heating demand can be spread more evenly.

FURTHER READING

- Baker, N. V.. *Energy and Environment in Non-Domestic Buildings: a Technical Design Guide*. Cambridge, Cambridge Architectural Research Ltd. for the RIBA, [1995]. 69 pp. A short guide to the principles of passive solar building, by the team that developed the LT Method.

- BS 5918:1989 *Code of Practice for Solar Heating Systems for Domestic Hot Water*. London, BSI, 1989.

- BS 8207:1985 *Code of Practice for Energy Efficiency in Buildings* . Amended Feb. 1994.

- Halliday, S. P.. *Environmental Code of Practice for Buildings and their Services*. Bracknell, Building Services Research and Information Association (BISRIA), 1994. 130 pp. £40.00. Fax +44 1344 487575. Step-by-step checklist for sustainable practice, following the sequence for a new building from inception to hand-over. Then continues on through use, refurbishment, decommissioning, demolition and disposal. Aimed at clients, architects, project managers, quantity surveyors, facilities staff and building services engineers.

- Cambridge Architectural Research Limited. *Design Guides for Energy Efficient Non-Domestic Buildings*. Cambridge, Cambridge Architectural Research Ltd., 1994-95. A set of four to eight-page design guides and case studies for schools, colleges, offices, and hospitals. Available from BRECSU Enquiries Bureau, BRE, Garston, Watford, WD2 7JR. Tel +44 1923 664258 Fax +44 1923 664787.

- CIBSE Building Energy Code. Part 1 Guidance towards energy conserving design of buildings and services; Part 2 Calculation of energy demands and targets; Part 3 Guidance towards energy conserving operation of building and services; Part 4 Measurement of energy consumption and comparison with targets for existing buildings and services. London, Chartered Institution of Building Services Engineers, 1977. Reprinted 1988.

- Energy Centre Denmark. *Basic Aspects of Application of District Heating*. Energy Centre Denmark - OPET for the European Commission, [1992]. 20 pp. Free. Guidelines and case studies. Available from: Energy Research Group, University College Dublin, Richview, Clonskeagh, Dublin 14. Tel (01) 269 2750 Fax (01) 283 8908.

- Goulding, John R. , J. Owen Lewis, and Theo C. Steemers, Editors. *Energy in Architecture : The European Passive Solar Handbook* . London, Batsford for the Commission of the European Communities, 1992. 135 pp. IR£ 45.

- Istituto Cooperative Per L'innovazione. *Small-scale cogeneration in non-residential buildings*. Rome, ICIE - OPET for the European Commission, 1992. 20 pp. Free. Guidelines and case studies. Available from: Energy Research Group, School of Architecture, University College Dublin, Richview, Clonskeagh, Dublin 14. Tel (01) 269 2750 Fax (01) 283 8908.

- Latorre Beltrán, J. V. and Cuñat Martínez, G. *A Review of Cogeneration Equipment of Selected Installations in Europe*. Valencia, ivEn - OPET for the European Commission, 1992. 19 pp. Free. Guidelines and case studies. Available from: Energy Research Group, School of Architecture, University College Dublin, Richview, Clonskeagh, Dublin 14. Tel (01) 269 2750 Fax (01) 283 8908.

- Rhônalpénergie. *Development of District Heating - Two Contrasting Examples: Denmark and a French Region*. Rhônalpénergie - OPET for the European Commission, 1994. 34 pp. Free. Available from: Energy Research Group, School of Architecture, University College Dublin, Richview, Clonskeagh, Dublin 14. Tel (01) 269 2750 Fax (01) 283 8908.

COOLING

Cooling should not be a significant problem in Irish buildings. This Section lists steps that can be taken to avoid overheating in the first place, and sustainable approaches to handling it should it occur.

Mews buildings, Dublin, Grafton Architects

Air-conditioning is energy-intensive. An air-conditioned building may consume two to three times the energy used by a similar naturally ventilated one. In most building types it can be avoided.

Site conditions, particularly in relation to solar radiation and wind direction, have an impact on cooling load but will not, in themselves, lead to cooling problems. Unplanned solar gain resulting from poor design, and internal gains from people, lighting and equipment, are more likely to be the causes of overheating.

I NATURAL COOLING STRATEGIES

1.1 Minimise Unwanted Heat Gains

Reduce the use of artificial lighting and its associated heat emissions by maximising daylighting. Specify well-controlled energy-efficient lighting systems (see Section B.9 : Lighting). Control solar heat gain by the orientation and design of glazing and shading, particularly on east and west facades (see Sections B.6: Heating and B.5: Envelope).

Specify energy-efficient domestic appliances, office equipment and industrial or building services plant . They generate less waste heat, and also reduce electricity bills. Cluster heat-producing equipment away from people and consider local mechanical extract.

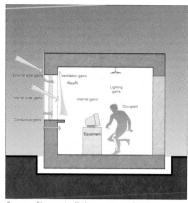

Sources of heat gains likely to cause overheating

1.2 Use Thermal Mass

Thermal mass within the building can absorb surplus heat during hot afternoons and re-emit it later in the evening or at night. This evens out the temperature gradient, reducing peak temperatures and providing useful heat after outdoor temperatures have fallen. An exposed concrete coffered ceiling can reduce peak temperatures by two or three degrees centigrade.

Thermal mass can also improve the utilisation factor for solar gains during the heating season (see Section B.6). However, in intermittently occupied buildings high thermal inertia can result in heat losses in winter. The optimum level of thermal inertia must be calculated for the particular circumstances.

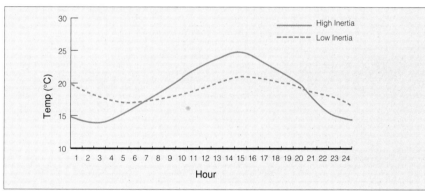

Internal temperatures on a hot day in buildings of high and low thermal inertia.

1.3 Design for Natural Ventilation

Outdoor air temperatures in Ireland are rarely too high for comfort, and well designed ventilation openings and controlled air-flow paths through the building can be used to cool the occupants and/or the building fabric (see Section B.8: Ventilation). If room temperatures are too high, a reasonable increase in air speed, without any change in temperature, will make people feel more comfortable by increasing the amount of heat they loose through convection.

If natural ventilation is being used to cool the building fabric, a flow of air should be directed across or through those elements of the building which have large thermal mass. There are now proprietary systems, for non-domestic buildings, which combine ventilation and thermal mass by circulating ventilation air through the cores of hollow concrete floor and roof slabs. In Summer, cool outdoor air is circulated through the structure at night. Then, during the day, fresh air is drawn through the cooled structure into the occupied spaces. Because of the small amounts of pre-cooled air needed to adjust room temperatures, constant fresh air can be supplied without noise or draughts. However, guidance on the design of thermal mass/night cooling systems, and on their applicability in different circumstances, is not well developed.

2 FANS

There may be circumstances in which energy-efficient fans are appropriate. A ceiling fan can produce the same cooling effect as a temperature reduction of 3°C, and at only one sixth the energy consumption of a typical air conditioning system (Baker, 1995). However, the air flows generated may be experienced as disagreeable by the occupants.

3 AIR CONDITIONING

If air-conditioning must be used, specify it only for those parts of the building where it is essential, and avoid refrigerants containing ozone-depleting chemicals. EU production of CFC (chloro-fluoro-carbon) refrigerants is to be phased out by 1997, and HCFCs (hydro-chloro-fluoro-carbons) on a phased basis thereafter . HFC (hydrofluorocarbon) refrigerants do not damage the ozone layer but are powerful greenhouse gasses, so still give rise to concern. Alternative refrigerants, which do not deplete ozone and which are not greenhouse gases include ammonia, propane, and water. Some, however, are hazardous and demand stringent safety procedures during installation, maintenance and disposal. The efficiency of the alternative refrigerants does not at present match that of the CFCs and HCFCs.

Many air-conditioning systems are designed for the worst case scenario, and therefore oversized for most of their working life. Allowing temperatures to rise above conventional comfort levels more often can reduce plant size and energy consumption considerably.

Effective maintenance is critical. Without it, efficiency falls and health problems increase.

FURTHER READING

- Halliday, S. P.. *Environmental Code of Practice for Buildings and their Services*. Bracknell, Building Services Research and Information Association (BISRIA), 1994. 130 pp. £40.00. Fax +44 1344 487575. Step-by-step checklist for sustainable practice, following the sequence for a new building from inception to hand-over. Continues on through use, refurbishment, decommissioning, demolition and disposal. Aimed at clients, architects, project managers, quantity surveyors, facilities staff and building services engineers.

- Centre for Renewable Energy Sources. *Natural and Low Energy Cooling in Buildings*. Athens, CRES for the European Commission, 1994. 20 pp. Free. Guidelines and case studies. Emphasis on School of Architecture, UCD, Richview, Clonskeagh, Dublin 14. Tel (01) 269 2750 Fax (01) 283 8908.

VENTILATION

The Green Building, Dublin, Murray O' Laoire

Ventilation is one of the more difficult issues in sustainable architecture. There is uncertainty about air-change rates, little well-researched design guidance, and measuring or controlling natural ventilation is problematic. However, the benefits of natural ventilation are substantial. This Section discusses the general principles and suggests some strategies.

As insulation levels improve, ventilation losses account for a higher proportion of heat losses. In a well-insulated house ventilation will account for over 50 percent of heat loss. Hourly air change rates due to unintended infiltration alone can vary from 0.1 or 0.2 in a tight, energy efficient building to 3.0 in a leaky building in windy conditions. The importance of controlling infiltration is evident, and the response has been to reduce ventilation rates and construct tightly-sealed buildings. However, there is increasing concern that lower ventilation rates are creating unhealthy conditions. There is also an alternative view, which is that increases in indoor pollutant sources, not reductions in ventilation rates, are the real problem. What is certain, however, is that in under-ventilated spaces mould spores and house dust mites thrive, and emissions from 'out-gassing' materials reach higher concentrations.

As we see in Section B.7: Cooling, an air-conditioned building may consume two to three times the energy used by a similar naturally ventilated one. It is also clear by now that in most circumstances people prefer to have windows that open, and that natural ventilation is healthier. The phenomenon of Sick Building Syndrome is observed almost exclusively in mechanically ventilated buildings (Baker, 1995)

1   VENTILATION REQUIREMENTS

Activities, processes and occupation densities determine which spaces are likely to need particular attention in terms of air temperature, relative humidity, odours, fumes or emissions.

Regulations made under the Safety, Health and Welfare at Work Act, 1989 require employers to ensure sufficient fresh air in enclosed places of work. What constitutes "sufficient" is not defined.

Requirement F1 of the Building Regulations requires that "adequate means of ventilation shall be provided for people in buildings". For dwellings, the Technical Guidance specifies how much ventilation is required for certain spaces, which spaces require natural ventilation, and which spaces may be mechanically ventilated. The guidance implies that uncontrolled permanent ventilation to dwellings is desirable. This is wasteful of energy. For other building types, the Guidance mentions *BS 5925: 1991, Code of Practice for Ventilation Principles and Designing for Natural Ventilation.*

RECOMMENDED FRESH AIR VENTILATION RATES, BS 5925: 1991.

Recommended outdoor air supply rates

[a] for a range of building types

Type of space	Smoking	Outdoor air supply l/s		
		recommended	minimum [take the greater value]	
		per person	per person	per m² floor area
factories	none	8	5	0.8
open plan offices	some			1.3
shops, department stores				
and supermarkets	some			3.0
theatres	some			-
dance halls	some	12	8	-
hotel bedrooms	heavy			1.0
laboratories	some			-
offices - private	heavy			1.3
residences [average]	heavy			-
restaurants [cafeteria]	some			-
cocktail bars	heavy	18	12	-
conference rooms [average]	some			-
residences [luxury]	heavy			-
restaurants [dining rooms]	heavy			-
board rooms, executive offices and conference rooms	very heavy	25	18	6.0
corridors		a per capita basis is not appropriate to these spaces.		1.3
kitchen [domestic]				10.0
kitchen [restaurant]				20.0
toilets				10.0

[b] recommended outdoor air supply rates for sedentary occupants

condition	recommended outdoor supply rate, l/s per person
with no smoking	8
with some smoking	16
with heavy smoking	24
with very heavy smoking	32

In some types of buildings, factories, garages, hospitals, large kitchens for example, ventilation is required for special applications such as removing heat, preventing contamination.

2   SITE CONDITIONS

Site conditions, particularly in relation to wind speed and direction, outdoor air quality and outdoor noise levels, influence the feasibility of using natural ventilation strategies.

Any natural ventilation system is affected by the speed and direction of wind on the site, and these are usually variable. The movement of air across the site will be from zones of high atmospheric pressure on the side exposed to the wind, through openings in the building, to low-pressure zones on the sheltered side. It is possible to increase or redirect external wind flows by manipulating the site, but in the Irish climate this should rarely be necessary. Designing to maximise shelter and minimise heat loss will more often be the priority.

3   VENTILATION IN DWELLINGS

Ventilation in houses is fairly straightforward. As fabric heat losses are reduced, ventilation losses dominate and providing adequate, but controlled, winter ventilation is the principal issue.

The familiar precaution of providing a gas, oil or wood burning appliance with its own combustion air supply, rather than drawing air from inhabited spaces, helps to maintain reasonably constant air pressure within the building envelope and reduce unwanted infiltration. Trickle vents provide sufficient winter ventilation for most rooms. A 100 mm vertical soil pipe with an outlet at ridge height can provide effective ventilation for a kitchen or bathroom; the temperature difference drives the system. In Scandinavian countries, where pressure testing of the building to check infiltration is common practice, simple mechanical systems with heat recovery are often used for ventilation.

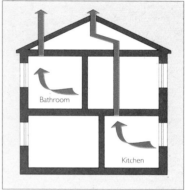

Stack ventilation in dwellings

4   VENTILATION IN NON-DOMESTIC BUILDINGS

Achieving good rates of natural ventilation in non-domestic buildings, while maintaining thermal comfort, fire separation, security and acoustic performance, is not easy, and has implications for the distribution of spaces and uses in plan and in section. Shallow buildings are, naturally, easier to ventilate, but airflow has to be considered in three dimensions. Thermal buoyancy and stratification in large internal spaces, such as factories, atria or auditoria, present particular problems of over or under ventilation. Conventional ventilation techniques may be wasteful, but there is little guidance on alternative techniques.

If energy efficiency and air quality criteria are both to be met, the ventilation system must be very well designed. Calculating likely air flows under varying conditions at the design stage is difficult, but software programmes such as BREEZE (see Section C.1: Tools for Design and Evaluation) are making the task more manageable.

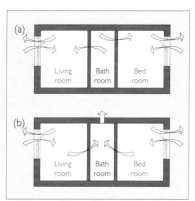

(a)Ineffective and (b)effective ventilation arrangements

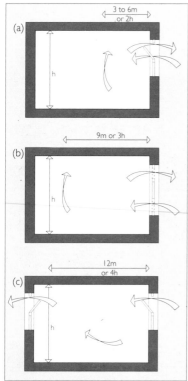

Effective depth for (a)single sided single openings, (b) single sided double openings, and (c) cross ventilation.

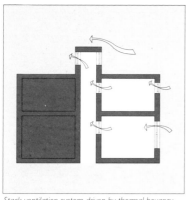

Stack ventilation system driven by thermal boyancy

5   NATURAL VENTILATION STRATEGIES

Air movement is greatest when the openings by which air leaves the building are larger than the air inlets, and the best distribution of fresh air is achieved when openings are diagonally opposite each other. When ventilating for air quality, as opposed to cooling, it is important to plan the path of air movement so as to avoid creating still pockets of stale air. The risk of planned ventilation paths being obstructed by subsequent alterations in internal layout should be considered. It is also clearly necessary to avoid situations where ventilation paths draw air from kitchens, bathrooms or processing areas through occupied spaces.

Some pragmatic rules of thumb for natural ventilation configurations, based on proposals made by Cambridge Architectural Research Limited (Baker, 1995), follow.

5.1   General Principle

Distribute openings widely. Openings on different facades, and widely distributed over any one facade, will be at different pressures. This helps to ensure that air flows will be well distributed in the building.

5.2   Single Sided Ventilation

Single sided ventilation, with high level openings only, is generally effective up to depth of 3 to 6 metres, or about twice floor to ceiling height. If there are openings at high and low level it can be effective up to a depth of 9 metres.

5.3   Cross Ventilation

Cross ventilation is generally effective up to 12 metres or four times room height. Deeper zones can be cross ventilated, but bear in mind that heat and pollutant levels in the air will build up as it moves across the space from inlet to outlet.

5.4   Stack Ventilation

In deeper buildings the 'stack effect' can be exploited. As air heats up and rises it must be replaced by denser, cooler air. If there are openings at the top of the building to vent the warmer air, and inlets at each level, the stack effect combined with negative air flow over the roof will generate a flow of fresh air through the building. For the forces of buoyancy to act there must be a significant temperature difference between the outgoing and incoming air. Internal gains will generally create the required difference. Buoyancy can be increased by using solar gain to heat air in unoccupied spaces - an atrium for example. This produces a 'solar chimney' effect. Air flows in stack ventilation are complex and there are no rules of thumb for dimensions. Physical models or computer simulation may be necessary.

5.5   Underfloor Supply

Ducted or underfloor supply can be used to cross ventilate double banked rooms. It is predominantly wind driven, so should be configured to respond to prevailing wind directions.

6   HEATING VENTILATION AIR

In this climate achieving adequate winter ventilation without reducing internal air temperatures, or causing local draughts, is a universal problem. If the required air change rate is low, trickle ventilation can satisfy the demand, but if it is high then the incoming fresh air must be warmed. Sunspaces (see Section B.6: Heating) can sometimes be used to heat or pre-heat ventilation air. A similar principle operates in some complex window types, where a layer of air within the glazing unit is heated by solar gain and allowed to circulate into the occupied space.

Integrating the building's structural framework and its ventilation system is another option. The thermal mass of hollow concrete floor and roof slabs can be used to store heat generated by solar and internal gains, and to warm fresh air drawn through voids in the slabs. In mild conditions this may be sufficient. In colder weather additional heat from conventional systems will be required.

7   NOISE

Noisy outdoor conditions present a problem for natural ventilation. Staggered opening double windows, acoustic-attenuating ventilators and glazed angled reflectors can reduce noise penetration.

8   CONTROLS

Carbon dioxide levels in the air, which are easy to measure, tend to rise as air quality decreases. Using CO_2 sensors to trigger automated ventilation dampers is an option in non-domestic buildings. Humidistats can be used to trigger ventilation in kitchens and bathrooms and other areas at risk of high relative humidity.

Managing a natural ventilation system can be a more complex business than controlling a wholly mechanical one. Variability in wind speed and direction makes precise control virtually impossible. In addition, since the rate of ventilation required in any space can vary with occupancy levels or personal preferences, some form of local occupant control of ventilation rates is desirable. This may have repercussions in other parts of the building and cut across the intended operation of the system, so that educating, and reminding, the occupants about how the building works becomes particularly important.

9   FAN ASSISTED AIR MOVEMENT

Where natural air movement within the building is insufficient, fans can be used to assist its flow. 'Hybrid systems' which combine natural ventilation with automated fans and vents can be used, for example, to counteract stratification, or to boost an underfloor supply when the wind direction is unfavourable. An advantage of fan driven systems is that it is possible to measure air flow with reasonably accuracy. This can be particularly useful in multi-occupancy spaces where, because of peoples' reluctance to open windows in cold weather, ensuring adequate levels of winter ventilation frequently presents problems.

10   MECHANICAL VENTILATION

Natural ventilation is not always feasible. Building layout, a noisy or heavily polluted external environment, the need for very high air-change rates or very pure air, may make mechanical ventilation unavoidable. In this case heat recovery should be considered.

An air-to-air heat exchanger can recover 80 percent of the differential between incoming and exhaust air. This is more energy efficient than an open window admitting cold or polluted air. For a heat recovery system to be cost-effective the building must be very well sealed.

For mechanical ventilation of particular spaces, in an otherwise naturally ventilated building, local fresh-air fan coil units can be effective, providing heating, cooling and ventilation.

11   INDOOR PLANTING

There is increasing evidence that plants absorb common indoor pollutants such as formaldehyde, trichloroethylene, benzene and carbon monoxide. It was found by the U. S. National Space and Aeronautics Administration (NASA) that ordinary varieties of house plants could remove up to 87 percent of pollutants within 24 hours, and that one house plant per 110 m^2 was sufficient to keep clean the air in the average home or office. (Wood and Burchett, 1995; Rattenbury, 1990)

FURTHER READING

- BS 5925: 1991, Code of Practice for Ventilation Principles and Designing for Natural Ventilation . London, HMSO, 1991. The code covers general principles of ventilation and natural ventilation, and discusses fresh air requirements for human respiration, dilution or removal of pollutants, humidity control, fuel burning appliances, thermal comfort, and smoke clearance from accidental fire.

- "Green buildings: ideas in practice - debating natural ventilation" in Building Services, January 1994, pp. 18-22. A discussion on the problems and potential of natural ventilation.

- Guidelines for Ventilation Requirements in Buildings, (Report 11, European Collaborative Action - Indoor Air Quality and its Impact on Man.) Brussels, European Commission, Directorate General for Employment, Industrial Relations and Social Affairs, 1992. 36 pp. Guidance on risks and standards for various indoor pollutants, building types and occupancy rates.

- Sick Building Syndrome: A Practical Guide. (Report 4, European Collaborative Action - Indoor Air Quality and its Impact on Man.) Luxembourg, European Commission, 1989. 36 pp. Risk factors associated with various indoor pollutants, with guidelines, checklists and questionnaires for conducting building investigations.

LIGHTING

Charlesland Golf Club, Co. Wicklow, Paul Keogh Architects

Getting daylight into buildings carries costs, but the light source is free, and a well designed daylight system consumes considerably less energy and less money than artificial lighting does. This Section offers guidance on optimising natural lighting, but also includes strategies for increasing the efficiency of the artificial lighting systems which are necessary in every building.

Lighting in buildings accounts for 5 per cent of Ireland's primary energy consumption. In non-domestic buildings lighting uses, on average, 18.4 per cent of the primary energy used for services. The equivalent figure for residential buildings is 5.4 per cent. However, in some building types - offices, for example - artificial lighting can account for more than 50 percent of total energy use.

Daylight availability corresponds with working hours during most of the year and daylight intensity generally exceeds, by a large margin, the interior lighting levels recommended for most activities. At Valentia, Co. Kerry. outdoor illuminance during working hours ranges from 5,000 to over 60,000 lux. Recommended illuminance levels for most indoor activities range from 100 to 1000 lux; only high precision industrial tasks require higher levels.

The directional quality of daylight provides good modelling of surfaces, and its spectral composition provides good colour rendering. Both of these factors help visual discrimination and so reduce the actual intensity of light required for a task. People actively enjoy daylight and sunlight, and the views of sky or landscape that come with them. It may be for these reasons that people accept greater variation in light intensity in naturally lit spaces than they are prepared to tolerate from artificial lighting systems.

The disadvantages of daylight are its unpredictability, and the risk of excessive heat losses or heat gains through large glazed openings.

Almost all spaces need artificial lighting after dark, and some spaces and activities will need it at all times. But good design, specification and maintenance practices for artificial lighting can produce very large savings in costs and energy. In non-domestic buildings 30 - 50 percent savings over conventional artificial systems are readily achieved, and 60 - 70 percent savings are not unusual.

Daylighting is heavily dependent on site conditions, on building form and on the relationship between fenestration and the size and proportions of interior spaces. Good decisions made in the early design stages pay off.

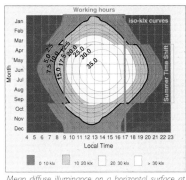

Mean diffuse illuminance on a horizontal surface at Valentia, Co. Kerry. Source: Laboratoire des Sciences Humaines, LASH-ENTPE, Lyon.

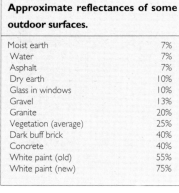

Approximate reflectances of some outdoor surfaces.	
Moist earth	7%
Water	7%
Asphalt	7%
Dry earth	10%
Glass in windows	10%
Gravel	13%
Granite	20%
Vegetation (average)	25%
Dark buff brick	40%
Concrete	40%
White paint (old)	55%
White paint (new)	75%

1   SITE

Local site conditions, particularly in relation to slope, orientation, and obstructions to light, have a major influence on the availability of light (see Sections B.3: Site and C.1: Tools for Design and Evaluation).

The reflectance of materials on the ground plane and on nearby vertical or inclined surfaces also contribute significantly to the levels of daylight that can be achieved inside a building. The white facade of a neighbouring building may help, by raising interior daylight levels, or may hinder, by causing glare. The surface reflectance of structures on or near the site can be measured on site with a reflectometer.

Within the site boundaries, of course, the design team can specify finishes which will exploit this phenomenon to the building's advantage.

2   LIGHTING LEVELS

The Building Regulations impose no requirements in respect of daylight levels or sunlight penetration in buildings. Regulations made under the Safety, Health and Welfare at Work Act, 1989 require employers to ensure that places of work shall, as far as possible, receive sufficient natural light, but also that windows, rooflights and glass partitions be such that excessive effects of sunlight in places of work are avoided. There is no guidance on how these requirements may be met.

The table alongside shows recommended levels of daylighting for the primary working areas of some building types. Other areas of these buildings may require higher or lower levels.

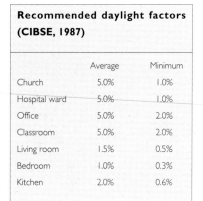

Recommended daylight factors (CIBSE, 1987)		
	Average	Minimum
Church	5.0%	1.0%
Hospital ward	5.0%	1.0%
Office	5.0%	2.0%
Classroom	5.0%	2.0%
Living room	1.5%	0.5%
Bedroom	1.0%	0.3%
Kitchen	2.0%	0.6%

Establish the lighting requirements for the particular occupants and activities planned for the building. Is one hundred per cent daylighting during working hours essential or is supplementary artificial acceptable? Must daylight in some rooms be filtered, or even excluded entirely? In some spaces fairly uniform lighting is required; in others variety is desirable. Design criteria will be more stringent for spaces where people occupy fixed positions - classrooms or hospital wards, for example - than for those in which people are free to move about.

3   DAYLIGHTING STRATEGIES

In addition to site conditions, the other critical factors in daylighting design are building form, room proportion, fenestration, and the reflectance of interior surfaces. Because light is geometric in its behaviour, optimising daylight penetration has fundamental implications for the siting, orientation, plan and section of a building.

3.1   Position on Site

To make a rough assessment of the effect of external obstacles on daylight availability use the procedure shown below for any face of the building where overshadowing may be an issue. The dimensions assume a room height of 2.7m and a room depth of 4m.

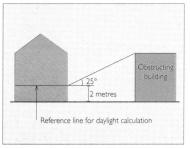

Angular criterion for spacing of buildings. For existing buildings, the reference height is the middle of the lowest window. Source: Littlefair, 1991.

If no obstruction subtends an angle greater than 25° to the horizontal, measured from the centre of the lowest window, then adequate levels of interior daylight should be achievable, though sunlight may be substantially reduced. Even if the angle is more than 25°, good daylighting may still be possible if the obstruction is narrow enough to allow light around its sides. If not, then consider an alternative position for the building, site conditions permitting. (Littlefair, 1991).

Where part of a building faces into a courtyard, an atrium or a narrow street, rooms near the ground are likely to have reduced daylight levels. Solutions include decreasing room depth, increasing room (and window) height, or providing larger areas of glazing.

3.2 Building Form

Allocating appropriate positions and orientations at the outer skin of the building to all of the spaces for which daylight and sunlight are essential can present planning problems, and conflict with other design objectives. Plan form and section are critical.

In a conventional building we can expect to find that daylight from vertical windows penetrates significantly about 4 to 6m from the external walls, with daylight levels decreasing as distance from windows increases. Roof-lighting, where it is possible, generates more uniform light distribution. This implies buildings which are single storey or narrow-plan or, if deep-plan, pierced with light-wells or courtyards. This tends to produce high surface-to-volume ratios, with increases in heat losses and in construction costs. The increasing use of the atrium is one design response to these problems.

3.3 Room Proportion

Generally a room will be adequately lit to a depth 2 to 2.5 times the height of the window head from the floor, so taller rooms can be daylit to greater depth.

If a room is lit from one side only, the depth of the room, 'L', should generally not exceed the value given by the equation:

$$[(L/W)+(L/H)] \leq (2/1-Rb)$$

where:
    W is the room width,
    H is the window head height above floor level,
    R_b is the average reflectance of surfaces in the rear of the room.

If 'L' exceeds this value the back of the room may appear gloomy, and supplementary daytime artificial lighting will be required.

3.4 Fenestration

3.4.1 Window Area and Orientation

Approximate glazing ratios for domestic and non-domestic buildings are given in Section B.6 : Heating. Thermal considerations should not outweigh the need for daylight in north facing rooms. For dwellings, the old by-law figure of 10 percent of room floor area for a habitable room may be a reasonable starting point. East and west facing windows, which in a non-domestic building may be problematic, can bring welcome morning and evening sunshine into a house.

In non-domestic buildings daylight requirements are likely to be more demanding. For office tasks such as reading and writing a window area of about 20 percent of room floor area may be needed to deliver sufficient daylight in a zone up to approximately 1.5 times the height of the room. It is unlikely that all of the spaces which need high levels of daylight can be accommodated on south-facing facades. However, the energy value of daylight received by glazing on a north facing facade may compensate for the heat losses through it. Windows on east and west facing facades are likely to cause overheating and will need some provision for shading.

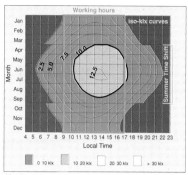

North

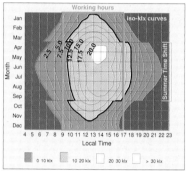

South

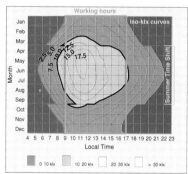

East

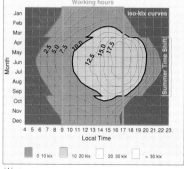

West

Mean diffuse illuminance on vertical surfaces, Valentia, Co. Kerry. (Note: The figures do not take account of any reflection for ground surfaces.) Source: Laboratoire des Sciences Humaines, LASH-ENTPE, Lyon.

Heating, cooling and lighting are, of course, interdependent, and unless they are carefully planned, large windows may produce unwanted heat losses and/or gains. But, while a conventional window, single-glazed with clear float glass will transmit approximately 85 percent of the light that falls upon it, installing double or triple glazing to reduce heat loss will reduce light transmission. (While the Building Regulations allow a trade-off between area and thermal transmittance, the visible transmittance of the glazing is not taken into account.) Where lighting requirements demand larger areas of glass than would be thermally satisfactory, specially treated glasses and glazing units may help to control heat losses or gains (see Section B.5: Envelope).

Low energy building, Hopkins and Ove Arup

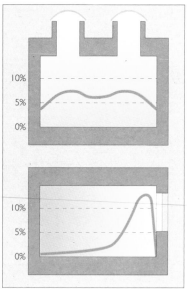

The distribution of light through top lighting and side lighting

3.4.2   Window Position and Slope

A horizontal rooflight is proportionately three times more effective as a source of daylight than a vertical window. This is because there is a substantial difference between levels of diffuse illuminance on horizontal surfaces and on north, south east and west facing vertical surfaces.

However, the disadvantage of horizontal or sloped glazing is that it collects more light and heat in summer than in winter. This is usually the opposite of what is needed. Vertical or near-vertical windows, which maximise sunlight penetration in winter, are generally preferable. (If a space is to be rooflit, consider clerestory, saw-tooth or other rooflight configurations in which the glazing is vertical.)

Rooflighting distributes light effectively. Windows in the upper part of a wall cast light farther into a room than does low-level glazing. Glazing on opposite sides of a room generally provides excellent lighting.

Particular site conditions, such as orientation or site boundaries, may inhibit the optimisation of window size and position. Conflicts between daylighting requirements and other factors - site orientation, noise, views, thermal requirements, fire regulations, planning laws, security, privacy - can often be resolved by detailed window design. Glass types and shading mechanisms together with transparent insulation, prismatic glazing assemblies and other daylighting devices, are covered in Section B5: Envelope.

3.4.3   Daylight Distribution

The distribution of light is often more important than the absolute quantity of light in a space. Peoples' general perception of room brightness is influenced by the evenness of lighting levels. Unless the intention is to create dramatic patterns of light, windows or rooflights should be spaced to give fairly even distribution. For rooflights a spacing of 1.0 to 1.5 times ceiling height is usually appropriate, and the distance between any wall and the nearest rooflight should generally not exceed half the distance between rooflights.

The light gradient across a room is significant. If there is too great a difference between daylight levels beside the windows and away from them, people some distance from the window will tend to switch on the lights, even though the daylight illuminance level in their part of the room may be functionally adequate.

For rooms which are deep, of unusual geometry, or which have particularly demanding daylight requirements it may be appropriate to calculate daylight factor distribution. Spot checks of daylight factor (see paragraph 4.2) at critical points may be sufficient, but in some cases more extensive studies may be necessary.

3.4.4   Interior Surfaces

Keep the reflectance of room surfaces as high as possible. The daylight entering a space is reflected repeatedly off walls, floor, ceiling and fittings, with some of its energy being absorbed each time. A smooth, brilliant-white wall may reflect 85 percent of the light that falls upon it; a cream wall 75 percent and a yellow one only 65 percent. 'Bright' colours, such as orange or vermilion, absorb as much as 60 percent of the light that falls upon them but, on the other hand, may create an impression of warmth in places the sunlight cannot reach.

Dark floor colours reduce light levels in a room but will increase the amount of solar radiation absorbed by the floor, helpful if the building structure is being used as a thermal store (see Section B.6: Heating).

Recommended reflectance of room surfaces	
Ceilings	0.7 - 0.85
Walls close to light sources (including windows)	0.6 - 0.7
Other walls	0.4 - 0.5
Floors	0.15 - 0.3

3.5   Sunlight

Sunlight is usually desirable, provided that it does not cause overheating or glare. People enjoy the sparkle that it brings to a building and for many building types some sunlight penetration is almost essential. Residential buildings and schools are two of the more obvious examples.

3.6   Glare

Only a few people in a space need experience glare for all the blinds to be closed and the lights switched on.

Plan the position, orientation and shading of windows to screen the sun from direct view. Windows at or near focal points (beside blackboards or in line with VDUs, for example) should be avoided.

Window glare is less likely to occur if light levels in the room are reasonably high. Additional light sources - rooflights, windows in an adjoining or opposite wall, or, less ideally, supplementary artificial lighting - counteract glare. Light coloured room finishes help, and brightness contrast in a window wall should be minimised by splaying window mullions and reveals, and by keeping that wall a pale colour.

4   EVALUATING DAYLIGHTING PROPOSALS

The techniques described below measure light alone. During the initial design stage the LT Method can be used to give a rough indication of the glazing ratios for facades and roof which will lead to minimum total (heating, lighting and cooling) energy consumption. At a more advanced design stage, computer models may be used to assess overall energy loads and interior conditions more accurately. (See Section C.1: Tools for Design and Evaluation.)

4.1   Models

Because light behaves virtually independently of scale, scale models give accurate results. Provided that the model is viewed under natural lighting conditions identical to those on the site, and its surfaces have the correct reflectances, luminances and illuminances will reach the same values in the model as they will in reality. Models are particularly useful for making quick comparisons of alternative design options.

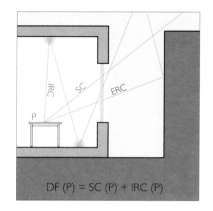

$$DF(P) = SC(P) + IRC(P)$$

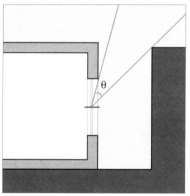

θ is the angle of visible sky measured from the centre of the window.

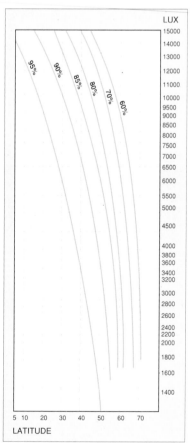

Outdoor light between 9 am and 5 pm as a function of site latitude (Daylight, CIE, 1970.)

4.2   Daylight Factor

The measure used in daylight design is the daylight factor (DF), defined as the indoor daylight illuminance at a given point as a percentage of illuminance outdoors under a standard sky. Recommended minimum daylight factors for a variety of spaces were shown in paragraph 2.

The daylight factor at any point on a working plane is calculated in terms of light coming directly from the sky (the Sky Component), light reflected from outside surfaces (the Externally Reflected Component), and light reflected from surfaces within the room (the Internally Reflected Component). Using a BRE Daylight Protractor (see Section C.1) daylight factor distribution can be plotted for any space or set of spaces at the design stage, but it is a time consuming process if done manually. Software programmes can be helpful at this stage. Spot checks for daylight factor levels can be helpful in some situations (see paragraph. 3.4.3 above).

4.3   Average Daylight Factor

In the early design stages the average daylight factor provides a useful technique for quickly assessing, from drawings, the daylight potential of a critical or representative space - a classroom or a cellular office, for example - which is to be repeated many times in a building. The average daylight factor (df), a measure of indoor daylight illuminance in a space as a percentage of illuminance outdoors under standard overcast conditions, is defined in the table below.

If a predominantly daylit appearance is required during the working day, then df should be 5 percent or more. If supplementary artificial lighting is acceptable, then 2 percent should be adequate.

$$df = (E_{in} / E_{out}) \times 100\%$$

where
E_{in} is the average interior illuminance and E_{out} is the unobstructed horizontal outdoor illuminance.

It can be calculated using the following formula:
$$df = TA_w \, \theta \, / \, [A \, (\, 1\text{-}R^2)] \, \%$$
where
T is the diffuse visible transmittance of the glazing, including corrections for dirt on glass and any blinds and curtains. (For clean, clear single glass a value of 0.8 can be used).
A_w is the net glazed area of the window (m²).
A is the total area of the room surfaces: ceiling, floor, walls and windows (m²).
R is their average reflectance. (For fairly light coloured rooms a value of 0.5 can be taken.)
θ is the angle of visible sky in degrees, measured from the centre of the window

4.4   Daylight Availability Frequency Curves

If daylight factor distribution has been plotted, daylight availability curves can be used to estimate the percentage of the working year during which daylight alone will provide the required amount of light.

For any space there is a critical level of outdoor illuminance which is necessary if the desired interior illuminance is to be achieved. For example, to achieve 400 lux at a point indoors where the daylight factor is 3.5 percent, the outdoor illuminance must be 400 divided by .035, or approximately 11,500 lux .

Using the daylight availability curves prepared by the Commission International de l'Eclairage (C.I.E.), it can be seen that if the building were located in Dublin, Latitude 53.26, 11,500 lux will be exceeded for only 65 percent of the time between 9 am and 5 pm. If this is were an office building, and supplementary lighting was to be avoided, some redesign would be necessary.

5   DAYLIGHTING DEVICES

5.1   Atria and Lightwells

The atrium is one response to the problem of getting daylight into deep plan buildings without incurring large heat losses. Its daylight performance is complex and depends on orientation and geometry, wall and floor surfaces, and the nature of its roof and glazing.

More direct daylight reaches the floor in wide, shallow, square atria than in deep, narrow, rectangular ones. Putting a glass roof over an open court will reduce daylight levels in the court by at least 20 percent and sometimes by 50 percent or more. The structure of the atrium roof should minimise obstructions to the glazing area, and its connections to the building should allow light to wash the atrium walls.

Dark finishes reduce internal reflectance, and the deeper the atrium the more important this becomes. Windows in the atrium walls also reduce reflectance. The upper walls are the most critical in reflecting incoming light down into the atrium, so limit the size and number of windows in this area.

The reduction in transmission heat loss through the separating walls means that the glazing ratio in these walls can be increased. Rooms at the upper levels may need protection from glare. Those at the base need to maximise the amount of light they receive but may have more uniform light distribution and avoid glare. (For the thermal performance of an atrium see Section B.6.)

The behaviour of light in lightwells and courtyards follows the same principles.

Office atrium, Dublin, Gilroy Mc Mahon.

5.2   Lightshelves

A lightshelf placed at the window opening above eye level, redirects incoming light onto the ceiling and shades part of the room close to the window. Its underside may also redirect light from a high-reflectance exterior ground surface onto the floor inside the room. The total amount of daylight entering the room will often be less, but its distribution will be more uniform, giving the impression of daylight penetrating deep into the space.

A lightshelf is most efficient when it is external, causes minimal obstruction to the window area, has specular reflective surfaces, and is combined with a high ceiling of high surface reflectance.

The sun-shading and glare-control functions of a fixed lightshelf are least effective for low-angle sun. In Ireland lightshelves should generally be considered only if glare is a problem, or window size is restricted and room surfaces, other than ceilings, must be of low reflectance.

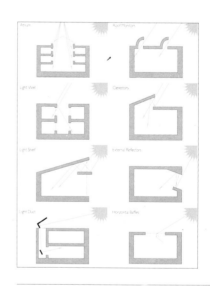

5.3   Lightpipes and Lightducts

Sunlight is collected by fixed or sun-tracking mirrors, concentrated by means of further mirrors or by lenses, then directed to the core of the building through mirrored shafts, acrylic rods or fibre-optic cables. Energy-efficient back-up lamps fixed at the head of the shaft substitute for sunlight during overcast conditions. They are cost-effective only if blue skies can be guaranteed for much of the year and so are unlikely to be appropriate in Irish conditions.

Source	Efficacy (lm/W)
Candle	0.1
Oil lamp	0.3
Original Edison lamp	1.4
Modern incandescent lamp	8-20
Tungsten halogen lamp	16-20
Flourescent lamp	31-102
Mercury lamp	30-60
Metal halide lamp	70-100
High pressure sodium	50-130
Low pressure sodium	120-140
Natural daylight	110

Luminous efficacy of various light sources

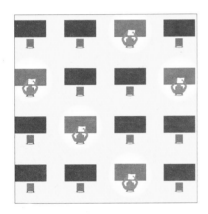

6   ARTIFICIAL LIGHTING

An energy-efficient artificial lighting system has two characteristics: the installation is energy-efficient in itself, and the lights remain off as long as there is sufficient daylight.

6.1   Lighting Installation

- Keep ambient lighting levels as low as the activity permits. Conventional practice is to provide illuminances in the range 100 lux, for corridors, to 1500 lux for high-precision work areas. Tables of recommended lux levels are familiar and readily available. In some countries, however, lower levels are now being considered (see Section B.1: Comfort).
- Use task lighting where appropriate; for localised high-acuity tasks, or for intermittently occupied work stations in an open office layout, for example.
- Specify energy-efficient lamps.
- Specify efficient luminaires. Efficiencies of 75-80 percent used to be exceptional, but are now usual.
- Specify appropriate luminaires. Design has a significant effect on amount, direction and quality of light.
- Specify high-frequency (HF) control gear. This increases the luminous efficacy of fluorescent lamps, doubles their life span, and reduces maintenance costs. It also improves light quality, eliminates flicker, and facilitates dimming.
- Specify dimmable fittings. Conventional lighting practice over-specifies to compensate for the fall-off in light output over the life of the equipment. Dimmable fittings linked to light sensors will reduce excess output / consumption during the early years.

6.2   Controls

Lighting controls are essential. In a conventionally lit commercial building, controls alone can make a 30 to 40 percent saving in lighting use. A range of devices is described below, but care in the design of control systems is necessary. Technical difficulties with the positioning and sensitivity of sensors, rapid changes in daylight levels due to fast-moving clouds, and the response of the occupants must all be allowed for.

- Limit the number of light fittings controlled by any one switch
- Provide for clear and understandable layouts for light switch panels.
- Zone light fittings and controls in relation to distance from windows
- Make light switches accessible. Pull-cord switches can be used where there are no nearby partitions. Hand-held remote control switches are useful in the same circumstances or where changes in partition layout are frequent. Simple local switching of this kind can produce 20 percent energy savings.
- Use Automated Controls
  - Timers can switch off lights at end of shift. Workers returning will probably turn on lights again only if they are still necessary.
  - Time delay switches turn off the light after a predetermined interval.
  - Movement sensors or sound detectors signal when a space is occupied. Most often used in intermittently used spaces, such as toilets, storerooms and some circulation areas.
  - Daylight sensors prompt switching or dimming of artificial lighting in response to daylight levels.
  - Voltage/current controls can be used in large areas which are intermittently occupied - warehouses for example. Once the luminaires have reached full output, the voltage/current control will reduce the energy input by 10 to 20 percent but lighting levels by only 5 percent to 10 percent. A movement detector linked to the system can ensure that the optimum lighting level is restored while anyone is working in the space.

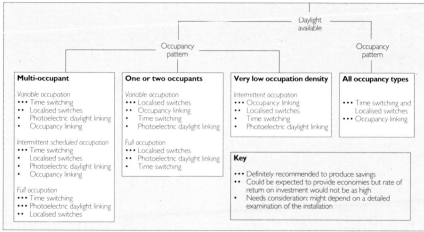

Multi-occupant	One or two occupants	Very low occupation density	All occupancy types
Variable occupation ••• Time switching •• Localised switches • Photoelectric daylight linking • Occupancy linking	*Variable occupation* ••• Localised switches •• Occupancy linking • Time switching • Photoelectric daylight linking	*Intermittent occupation* ••• Occupancy linking •• Localised switches • Time switching • Photoelectric daylight linking	••• Time switching and Localised switches ••• Occupancy linking
Intermittent scheduled occupation ••• Time switching • Localised switches • Photoelectric daylight linking • Occupancy linking	*Full occupation* ••• Localised switches •• Photoelectric daylight linking • Time switching		
Full occupation ••• Time switching ••• Photoelectric daylight linking •• Localised switches		**Key** ••• Definitely recommended to produce savings •• Could be expected to provide economies but rate of return on investment would not be as high • Needs consideration: might depend on a detailed examination of the installation	

Selecting a control system (CADDET. Saving energy with efficient lighting in commercial buildings, 1995)

In buildings of complex or sophisticated daylight design, particularly those with exterior adjustable daylighting devices, integrated automatic control systems are probably essential.

Any control system needs to be well structured. The results of a Building Research Establishment study on the use of lighting controls makes the case for a realistic assessment of user response (see Section B.13: Ensuring Good Performance).

Automated controls

7 SUPPLEMENTARY LIGHTING

Where artificial lighting is used to supplement daylighting it should be designed to support the directional quality of daylight. Specify lamps with colour appearance and colour rendering qualities that correspond with the character of daylight in the space. If these conditions are met, and there is an average daylight factor of 2 percent or more, the room will normally appear to be predominantly daylit.

8 MAINTENANCE

Dirty windows, dusty luminaires and grubby walls will reduce the effectiveness of both daylight and artificial light. Dirt on vertical windows can reduce performance by 10 percent or more, and there is no limit to the reduction in performance if dirt is allowed to build up on rooflights. Dust can reduce luminaire efficiency by 20 to 25 percent and poor maintenance of a typical fluorescent lighting installation can reduce performance by 50 percent in the space of three years. Plan for access and agree realistic maintenance schedules with the client.

Dunlaoghaire Fire Station, Dunlaoghaire Rathdown

FURTHER READING

- Baker, N., A. Fanchiotti and K. Steemers, Eds. *Daylighting in Architecture: A European Reference Book.* London, James & James for the European Commission, 1993. £60 Stg. Comprehensive text on the scientific and research background to the state of the art in daylighting analysis and design.

- BRECSU. *Energy Efficient Lighting in Schools*, 1992; *Energy Efficient Lighting in Industrial Buildings*, 1992. *Energy Efficient Lighting in Buildings*, 1993. *Energy Efficient Lighting in Offices*, 1993. *Energy Efficient Lighting Practice*, 1994. Garston, BRECSU-OPET for the Commission of the European Communities. A series of booklets containing concise design guidelines with case studies. Free.

- *BS 8206: 1992 Part 2 Code of Practice for Daylighting*, London, BSI, 1992.

- *CIBSE Applications Manual: Window Design.* London, Chartered Institution of Building Services Engineers (CIBSE), 1987. Detailed design guide.

- Crisp, V. H. C., P. J. Littlefair, I. Cooper and G. McKennon. *Daylighting as a Passive Solar Energy Option.* (BR 129) Garston, Building Research Establishment, 1985. Background study on the potential of daylighting in buildings.

- Eolas. *Energy Efficient Lighting.* Eolas Industrial Education Programme. Dublin, Eolas, [1993]. Study on potential of energy-efficient artificial lighting systems in Ireland.

- Irish Energy Centre. *Energy Efficient Lighting in Industry; Energy Efficient Lighting in Hotels; Energy Efficient Lighting in Offices; Energy Efficient Lighting in Shops; Energy Efficient Lighting in the Home.* Dublin, Irish Energy Centre for the European Commission, 1995. A series of one-page summaries by building type. Free.

- Littlefair, P. J. *Site Layout Planning for Daylight.* (BR 209). Watford, Building Research Establishment, 1991. Design guidelines.

- Littlefair, P. J.. *Site Layout Planning for Sunlight and Solar Gain.* (Information Paper IP 4/92) Garston, Building Research Establishment, 1992. Design guidelines.

- McNicholl, Ann and J. Owen Lewis, Eds. *Daylighting in Buildings.* Dublin, UCD - OPET for the European Commission, 1994. Free. Guidelines and case studies. Available from: Energy Research Group, School of Architecture, UCD, Richview, Clonskeagh, Dublin 14. Tel (01) 269 2750 Fax (01) 283 8908

- Slater, A. I.. and P. J.. Davidson. *Energy Efficient Lighting in Buildings.* Garston, BRECSU - OPET for the Commission of the European Communities, 1991. Free. Guidelines and case studies.

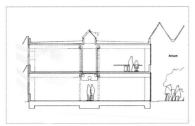

The Bruntland Centre, Denmark, KHR Architects. Windows incorporating adjustable prismatic louvres. PV panels mounted on facade.

WATER

Treating water for human consumption uses considerable resources. A great deal of treated water is wasted, or used for purposes which do not demand the same degree of purity. It is easy to make substantial savings in water use.

Despite relatively high levels of rainfall throughout the year summer water shortages in Ireland are not uncommon. Reservoirs are over-stretched and some water purification facilities are no longer able to match demand. Meanwhile, large volumes of water are wasted.

On average, Irish people use from 150 to 200 litres of water per day, 45 percent of it for flushing WCs. Urinals are the single most wasteful fitting in use. Most are designed to flush every 20 minutes, and continue to do so through the night, on weekends and over holiday periods, whether needed or not. Simply specifying water conserving sanitary fittings and appliances could reduce water consumption in residential buildings by at least 20 to 30 per cent, and in non-domestic buildings by 50 per cent or more.

I   WATER CONSERVATION STRATEGIES

I.I   Install Water Meters

In principle, a water meter should be installed in every new or retrofitted building, whether required by the Local Authority or not.

I.2   Specify Water Conserving Appliances

Because water-efficient fittings use less hot, as well as less cold, water they reduce water heating costs too.

Water using Appliance	Conservation Strategy
WCs	• Six litre flush toilets are now widely available and should be specified.
Urinals	• All urinal units should be fitted with infra-red motion detectors to control flushing.
Taps	• Taps should be fitted with pressure regulators, spray nozzles and sprung on/off control or infra-red detectors.
Shower Heads	• Specify low consumption heads.
Water heaters	• Units for heating water should be located close to the point of use. This will reduce the volume run off before the user gets hot water.
Clothes washers, dish washers, etc.	• Check water consumption of equipment to be purchased. There are significant variations in the quantity used by different models.

I.3   Minimise Hot Water Draw-Off

Careful planning to reduce the length of hot water pipe runs will cut the amount of cold water wasted before hot water reaches the taps. It will also reduce the amount of energy lost from hot water left in the pipes.

I.4   Plan Water Storage

Where large volumes of water storage are required, it is better to use tanks in series and fitted with by-pass valves. This avoids the need to drain the entire storage system when only one tank needs maintenance or modification.

I.5   Consider Dual Systems

For large commercial or industrial buildings consider a dual water supply system, with untreated water used for processing and cooling.

I.6   Use Groundwater

About 50 percent of Ireland's groundwater is reasonably accessible. Currently about 25 percent of water used is groundwater. If unpolluted, it is a good source of supply, naturally of good quality and needing little or no treatment. Development and distribution costs are low compared to those for surface reserves. The quality of drinking water is regulated by the EC Directive on the Quality of Water for Human Consumption, but there are no specific regulations on the sinking of wells. Local Authorities monitor quality in public and group water supply systems only. The Building Regulations themselves impose no specific requirements for quality, quantity or source of water for human consumption or use.

Heavy industrial use of groundwater can lower water levels over an aquifer, and affect neighbouring users. Determine the size of the resource before proceeding.

1.7   Conserve Rain Water

Consider reviving traditional practices by collecting rain water from roof surfaces for car washing, gardening and other outdoor purposes. (Note that water run-off from lead-based roofing materials cannot be used to irrigate vegetables.) Storage vessels need an overflow to a gulley in case of heavy rainfall, and a secure cover to prevent accidents to children. Rainwater can be stored in an underground tank, but then needs pumping to the surface. Arrangements should allow for some run-off before water is diverted to a storage tank. This prevents the dirt and debris washed off surfaces in the first few minutes of rainfall building up silt at the bottom of the tank.

Rainwater can be used to fill pools which are decorative and can also function as low-grade sources for heat pump coils, or as a source of water for fire-fighting. In all cases child safety is an issue.

In isolated areas the collection of rainwater for domestic use is viable, but needs to be approached carefully. The content of the rainwater itself, the surfaces over which it flows and the way in which it is filtered and stored determine its quality. Acid rain, asbestos, zinc or lead roofing materials, bird droppings and fungi are common causes of contamination.

1.8   Re-Use Water

The re-use of grey water (waste water discharged from sinks, basins, baths and washing machines) for WC flushing is sometimes suggested. However, because of the risk of cross-infection, it can be used in single-family houses only. Plumbing is straightforward. Properly treated grey water can be used for most horticultural purposes. (See also Section B.11: Wastes)

1.9   Minimise Irrigation

Avoid planning landscape features which will need irrigation during the summer, unless provision is being made for the storage of rainwater or re-use of grey water.

FURTHER READING

- ENFO. *Ground water*. (Briefing Sheet 3). Dublin, ENFO, 1995. Useful leaflet on protection of groundwater and procedures for accessing on-site groundwater supply.

- ENFO. *Water Supply* . (Briefing Sheet 22). Dublin, ENFO, 1995.

WASTES

Sound policies on waste are fundamental to sustainability. This Section reviews strategies for reducing waste at source or putting it to good use.

It is estimated that 85 percent of municipal waste in Ireland is potentially recyclable. The 1993 figure for household and commercial refuse was 1.68 million tonnes. Almost all of this, together with street litter, was collected by local authorities and went to landfill sites. About 7.4 per cent was recycled. Sewage treatment plants generate waste in the form of sludge, almost of half of which goes into the sea; most of the balance is dried and spread on agricultural land or disposed of in landfill sites. Current government policy is to reduce municipal waste by 20 per cent, through recycling, by 1999. The Waste Bill 1995, if enacted as proposed, would place greater responsibility for recycling on the producers, distributors and retailers of packaging waste.

The disposal of toxic and dangerous wastes, considered by the EU to be one of the greatest problems in environmental protection, is covered by the European Communities (Toxic and Dangerous Waste) Regulations, 1982. At present about 54 percent of Ireland's hazardous waste is recycled.

Construction debris, forestry and wood processing waste, metal scrap and unclassified industrial process wastes are collected by private firms who dispose of most of it in Local Authority or private landfill sites.

The development of more sustainable practices for construction and demolition wastes is heavily dependent on the existence of handling facilities and of a market for recycled materials. In The Netherlands, fixed processing sites for construction and demolition wastes recover for re-use an estimated 60 percent of material. Denmark, in 1993, achieved an 80 percent recycling rate for construction and demolition waste through landfill and materials tax incentives. (World Resource Foundation) There have been some discussions about the desirability of an EU Directive on Construction Waste, but no proposals have been put forward.

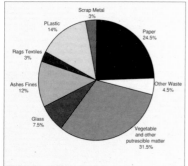

Types of waste disposed of by local authorities, excluding sewage sludge. Source: ENFO

1   WASTE STRATEGIES

There are four strands to any waste management strategy:
- reduce waste at source
- sort wastes
- re-use or recycle
- dispose of waste safely

WASTE GENERATION AND RECYCLING 1993
(Household and Commercial Wastes)

Material	Quantity Arising (Tonnes)	Quantity Recycled (Tonnes)	Recycling Rate (%)
Paper	382,000	73,000	19
Glass	107,000	22,000	21
Plastic	141,000	100	-
Metals	69,000	17,000	24
Textiles	83,000	12,000	14
Organic	573,000	20	-
Other	324,000	0	-
Total	**1,679,000**	**124,120**	**7.4**

Source: Recycling for Ireland. Department of the Environment, 1994

2   CONSTRUCTION WASTE

In Sweden it has been calculated that the construction of a ten storey building generates waste equivalent to the materials used in one full storey.

Design for standard sizes to reduce on-site cutting, require the contractor to use off-cuts to the feasible maximum, and plan for re-usable formwork. Enforcing the standard specification clauses on the handling, storage and protection of materials is one of the most effective ways of reducing site waste. Careful estimating and ordering procedures by the contractor can have a big impact. Surplus concrete and mortar, for example, are particularly difficult to dispose of.

Clauses requiring the separation, storage and collection of recyclable materials (including packaging), and the containment and disposal of other materials, can be written into the specification. Only eco-friendly cleaning materials should be used during construction and at final clean-up. Good waste management practices will involve additional labour costs, but should cut materials costs, and will certainly contribute to site safety.

Re-use building materials or components where possible and, when specifying products, favour those which incorporate recycled material. Tiles, bricks, slates, joinery, scrap metals, kitchen and bathroom fixtures all have a market. CFCs and oil in existing heating and air-conditioning systems can be recovered and re-cycled.

Re-using an existing building is one of the most effective sustainable strategies the client and design team can adopt. In addition to the savings in materials, and in the energy and pollution costs of production and transport arising from construction of a new building, there are savings on the services and infrastructure which would be needed for a building on a virgin site.

3 SOLID WASTES

The only time at which the design team is likely to have any influence on the generation of solid wastes is during the construction phase. However, the design team can contribute to sustainable housekeeping practices on the part of the occupants by planning safe and adequate storage for different categories of waste. This is the preliminary to recycling or to safe and efficient disposal.

In residential buildings kitchen and other organic wastes can be composted and used for gardening if occupiers are willing and interested. All dwellings should have space for the separate storage of recyclable materials - usually paper, glass, plastics and metals - to facilitate householders who wish to take advantage of recycling banks, or of recycling collection services where they exist. *Contact: ENFO, 17 St. Andrew St., Dublin 2. Tel (01) 679 3144*

In non-domestic buildings the collection of separated waste for recycling will probably have to be paid for by the occupier unless volumes are large, but the number of companies collecting materials for recycling is increasing. If the volume of a particular material is substantial it can be sold to a manufacturer who will carry collection costs. *Contact: ENFO, 17 St. Andrew St., Dublin 2. Tel (01) 679 3144*

If the scale of the project is very large, consider the feasibility of using solid waste to generate energy, perhaps in co-operation with other building owners in the area. (see Sections A.2.10 and B.5.6.4)

4 WATER-BORNE WASTES

The volume and content of sewage depends, of course, on occupation density and the nature of the activities carried on in a building. Water conservation measures will reduce the volume output, which is helpful, but there is not a lot that the design team can do about the content. Grease and oil cause problems at pumping stations - so traps should be specified where necessary. Bleach, detergents and other common cleaning materials increase the processing load at the Local Authority treatment plant, but, except during the construction phase, this is not within the control of the design team.

Providing for natural drainage on the site, by specifying low gradients and porous rather than impervious ground surfaces, will allow rainwater to percolate back into the soil instead of overloading sewage treatment plants.

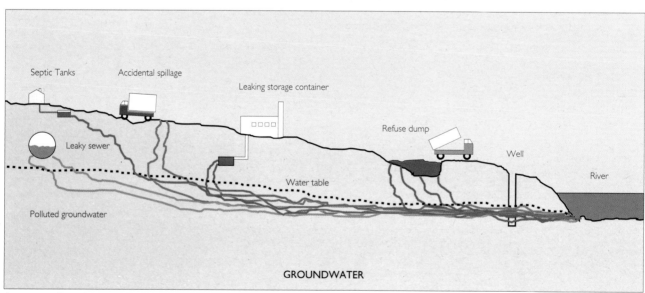

Some sources of groundwater pollution beneath urban areas

Reed Beds, in which septic tank effluent is filtered through a sand and gravel filled pit planted with selected species of native wetland reeds, are an eco-friendly alternative to the soakaway. The site area required is approximately 25m² for a typical family dwelling. Technically there is no reason why the bed should have to be located any further than ten metres from the house, but the Local Authority may require a distance of 25 metres. (This may change in the light of information from continental European countries, where there is extensive experience of reed bed use.) Provided that a three-chamber septic tank is specified, which may add 20 percent to tank costs, the outflow is clean enough to be discharged directly into any watercourse. The principal benefits are the reduction in site area needed, and the elimination of the risk of ground water contamination. In areas with high water tables, common in Ireland, reed beds may not be appropriate. *Contact: Dr. Uwe Hild, Poplar, Caherdaniel, Co. Kerry. Tel and Fax (066) 75285.*

The methane produced by septic tanks, by slurry pits, and by most Local Authority treatment plants in Ireland is vented to the atmosphere, but it could instead be burned to provide energy. Since methane is a greenhouse gas twenty times more damaging than carbon dioxide there is a double benefit in environmental terms. Tullamore Urban District Council has such a system in place and uses the energy for sewage processing. However, at present, the engineering and safety requirements make very small scale systems impracticable.

The potential for the re-use of water on site is limited (see Section B.10) However, if volumes are large and temperatures high, it is well worth considering reclaiming the heat by routing waste water discharged from sinks, basins, baths and washing machines through a heat exchange unit.

5   GRANTS

Under Circular ENV 4/89 grants are available to individuals and organisations establishing recycling projects. The maximum grant is 50 percent of capital cost, and the scheme is aimed at community and voluntary rather than commercial organisations. Contact: Waste Management Section, Department of the Environment, Customs House, Dublin I. Tel (01) 679 3377 Fax (01) 874 2710

FURTHER READING

- Construction Industry Research and Information Association. *Waste Minimisation and Recycling in Construction: a Review.* (SP 122). London, CIRIA, c. 1995. £44.00. International review of current state of practice and knowledge; identifies possibilities and constraints.

- Department of the Environment. *Recycling for Ireland: a strategy for recycling domestic and commercial waste.* Dublin, July 1994. 36 pp. Free. Summary of situation in 1993 and statement of public policy objectives.

- Environmental Resources Limited, in association with the Environmental Institute, UCD. *Towards a Recycling Strategy for Ireland.* Dublin, Department of the Environment, 1993. 91 pp. Free. Background study for formation of government policy.

- Triangle J Council of Governments. *WasteSpec: model specifications for construction waste reduction, reuse, and recycling.* Funded by the U. S.. Environmental Protection Agency. P. O.. Box 12276, Research Triangle Park, NC 27709, USA. 1995. Aims to help the design team choose measures appropriate to the project and provides specification clauses, with likely cost implications, to implement them. (Available on disc).

- World Resource Foundation. *Construction and Demolition Wastes.* (Information Sheet) Tonbridge, Kent, The World Resource Foundation, 1995. Tel +44 1732 368333 Fax +44 1732 368337

RETROFITTING

Warehouse conversion, Galway, Grafton Architects

Re-using an existing building is one of the most effective sustainable strategies there is. It saves the materials, energy and pollution costs involved in constructing a new building, and also the new services and infrastructure which might be needed for a virgin site. This Section looks at some of the implications of retrofitting and outlines the steps that can be taken to improve performance.

The replacement rate of the national building stock is less than two percent per year. Of the remaining 98 percent, any building which performs badly in terms of energy consumption, comfort conditions or environmental impact is a potential candidate for retrofitting. The economics of energy-saving measures for single-family dwellings are fairly well understood, but upgrading other building types involves assessing a range of options in increasing order of cost and complexity.

The benefits to owners and occupants of a thorough re-evaluation of a building's design and operation are potentially far-reaching: comfort, health, productivity, enjoyment, aesthetic quality, prestige, and capital value, together with reduced running costs and security from energy price fluctuations. Some of these benefits are difficult to quantify, but they are nonetheless apparent to clients.

1   TO RETROFIT OR NOT ?

Sometimes there will be a choice to be made between retrofitting an existing building and commissioning or buying a better building; sometimes retrofitting will be unavoidable. In either case there are similar questions to be answered. Can the required internal environment be achieved? How much energy will be saved? What will be the reductions in CO_2, CFCs and other pollutants ? Can the proposed measures be applied at no extra risk? Will they be durable? Will additional maintenance be required? Are there other, non-energy benefits? Will the measures be cost-effective?

An energy audit (see Section C.1.1) can give a useful insight into where energy is being used and which are the most promising opportunities for energy savings. As a preliminary step, calculating the building's Normalised Performance Indicator (Appendix 6) allows the design team to rate it in comparison with other buildings of the same type and to assess the scale of its potential for improvement.

The cost-effectiveness of any intervention will be increased if it is implemented in phase with the normal renewal cycle of the building and its fittings: running maintenance; routine redecoration and replacement of out-worn equipment; interior fit-out; or total building refurbishment. As with new-build, an integrated approach will produce better results than a piecemeal one.

If comfort conditions before retrofitting were poor, the energy conserved by retrofit measures may be absorbed by the improvement in living conditions. Fuel bills may fall, internal temperatures rise to acceptable levels, and condensation, mould growth and other problems disappear, while energy consumption remains unchanged.

In the case of buildings of heritage value a realistic attitude is needed. It may simply not be possible to achieve the comfort levels people normally expect without destroying the character of the building.

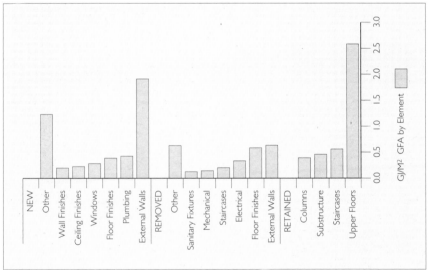

Embodied energy, per m² of ground floor area, in a refurbishment project. Source: Tucker & Treolar, 1994

2   CHOOSING RETROFIT STRATEGIES

In any sustainable retrofit programme there are two fundamental moves: reduce demand; and make sure that where additional resources are needed, they are supplied and used efficiently.

The objective is to implement these moves while simultaneously improving environmental quality

3 SERVICES

3.1 Space Heating and Ventilation

Reducing demand	Insulate fabric
	Reduce infiltration
	Utilise solar gain
	Consider heat recovery
Improving efficiency	Ensure efficiency of heating appliances
	Improve controls

3.2 Space Cooling and Ventilation

Reducing demand	Reduce solar overheating
	Improve efficiency of lighting and other heat-producing equipment
	Use natural ventilation
Improving efficiency	Ensure efficiency of pumps and fans
	Improve controls
	Specify efficient cooling plant (if cooling plant is unavoidable)

3.3 Lighting

Reducing demand	Improve daylighting
	Rationalise space usage
Improving efficiency	Re-design artificial lighting layout
	Specify efficient lamps, luminaires and ballasts
	Improve controls

3.4 Water

Reducing demand	Use water treated for human consumption only where necessary
	Improve water storage and pipe layout
	Install water meters.
Improving efficiency	Specify water conserving fittings

3.5 Building Management

Reducing demand	Educate building users
	Ensure good 'housekeeping'
Improving efficiency	Set targets and monitor performance
	Ensure effective maintenance and operation
	Consider a range of energy management systems

4   BUILDING ENVELOPE

Alternative forms of construction for the building envelope are covered in Section B.5. This section looks at the options which are likely to be relevant in retrofitting existing buildings. 'Upgrading' can cause, as well as solve, problems. Condensation in weather-tight buildings is a familiar one. So move with care.

4.1   Walls

Internal insulation should generally be used only if the facade must not be altered, occupancy is intermittent, or in multi-unit buildings where not all owners want to upgrade. It is usually cheaper than external insulation, but it reduces room size and involves the replacement of skirtings, architraves, pipework, wiring and any other items fixed to the external wall. It precludes use of the building's thermal mass as a heat store. Thermal stresses in the outer skin increase, the risk of interstitial condensation rises, and it is almost impossible to solve the problem of cold bridges.

External insulation is preferable if budget, climate and other circumstances permit. Capital costs are higher but, if renovation of the envelope is necessary anyway, payback can be as low as three years. It can improve the appearance, weather resistance and life of the wall, and may lower exterior maintenance costs. It allows the thermal mass of the building to be used as heat store. Detailing around openings, corners, parapets, eaves, or verges is likely to be problematic, but cold bridges can be eliminated. The building can remain occupied during installation.

Cavity fill has no effect on internal or outside appearance or on room size, and can be applied without disturbing the occupants. It allows the inner leaf to function as a thermal store and, depending on construction, can eliminate cold bridging. The insulation is well protected, and a range of proprietary systems are available. However, careful inspection to determine suitability is essential and it must be carried out by skilled operatives. Without a thermographic survey it is difficult to ensure that the wall is evenly insulated. Some zones may be impossible to insulate; wall-to-roof or column-to-beam junctions, head and sill positions, for example. Bridging the cavity may exacerbate damp penetration.

4.2   Roofs

Heat losses from roofs are high because of their relatively large surface area and because of night-time radiation to the sky. Adding insulation is usually relatively easy and pay-back periods are short. The insulation of domestic pitched roofs at joist or rafter level is well-understood, as is the need to avoid trapping moisture. If the roof finish is to be renewed the new insulation can be applied above the rafters, before tiles or membrane are replaced.

In general, proprietary pitched roof systems (such as the metal deck systems used in industrial premises, which may already have some insulation) can be upgraded by the application of additional internal insulation. These relatively durable decking systems are often in good condition and continue to provide an effective rain screen.

In flat roofs, cold deck construction should be avoided. Warm or inverted deck constructions allow the roof slab to act as a thermal store, and the risk of interstitial condensation is reduced. An inverted deck has the advantage of protecting a sound weatherproof layer against thermal stress, but, if the existing roof finish has reached the end of its useful life, a warm deck solution may have an attractive payback period.

4.3   Floors

The cost of placing insulation under existing concrete floors is not likely to be justified unless they need to be replaced for other reasons; damp, deterioration, or inadequate load-bearing capacity, for example. Heat loss can sometimes be reduced by ensuring effective land drainage around the building perimeter and adding external insulation below ground level. Another alternative is to place insulation over an existing floor and cover it with a screed or proprietary flooring system.

Suspended floors are usually easier to insulate and proprietary systems for various forms of floor construction are available.

4.4   Windows and Doors

Transmission losses through glazing, cold bridging through frames, and infiltration losses through joints are all issues to be addressed. Improvements in these areas will not only reduce building heat loss but, by eliminating draughts and the 'chill factor' of cold glazing, will also reduce the room temperature needed for comfortable conditions.

It is often possible to fit secondary glazing to existing frames with only minor adaptations. If there are existing double-glazed frames in good condition, replacing the existing glazing with units which incorporate a pane of 'low-e' glass or a gas-filled cavity may be appropriate, though the economics are unlikely to be attractive. Where frame size makes it impossible to accommodate double glazing, laminated glass - two sheets of glass with plastic film sandwiched between them - will give some improvement in insulation performance with little loss in light transmission. Insulated blinds or shutters are an inexpensive method of reducing heat losses after dark.

Transparent insulation materials (TIM) are getting cheaper, and may be an option for openings where heat losses outweigh heat gains but daylight is essential.

5   CONTROL SYSTEMS

Better controls can have a substantial impact on energy consumption and are sometimes valid as stand-alone options. Thermostatic radiator valves typically save 10 percent over manual controls. Individual meter-based billing reduces consumption by 15 percent in apartment buildings (Friedemann & Johnson, 1994). A metering and recording system will give owners or occupiers the information and motivation to manage their energy consumption. Generally the more efficient a control and metering system is, the higher its investment cost.

Sustained good management is essential. Controls left on a winter setting during the summer waste both energy and the capital cost of their installation.

6   STRATEGIES FOR HOUSING

Typical energy efficiency measures for existing housing (based on Davidson, 1994)		
Measure	Typical (simple) pay-back	Application
Hot water cylinder insulation	4 to 6 months	All dwellings with stored hot water
Low-energy lamps	1 to 2 years	All dwellings
Loft insulation	1 to 3 years	All dwellings with accessible lofts
Draught-stripping of window & doors	2 to 10 years	All dwellings (keeping adequate ventilation)
Condensing boiler	2 to 4 years	At replacement of old boiler
Cavity wall insulation	4 to 7 years	Dwellings with suitable cavity masonry walls
Double glazing	up to 12 years	Cost-effective when windows need replacing

7   STRATEGIES FOR INDUSTRIAL BUILDINGS

Typical energy efficiency measures for existing industrial buildings (Davidson, 1994)

Measure Typical savings		Pay-back (years)
Draught proofing	15 - 20%	1 - 5
Fabric insulation	0 - 15%	2 - 6
Boiler replacement	10 - 20%	1 - 4
Time / temperature control	5 - 15%	1 - 5
Destratification fans	5 - 20%	1 - 3
Fluorescent lights to replace tungsten	40 - 70%	1 - 3
High-frequency electronic ballast	15 - 20%	5 -15
Efficient luminaire reflectors	20 - 50%	2 - 6
Automatic lighting controls	20 - 50%	2 - 5
Localised lighting	60 - 80%	4 - 8
CHP	30 - 40%	3 - 6
BEMS	10 - 40%	1 - 5

8   GRANTS

The Irish Energy Centre operates an Energy Efficiency Investment Support Scheme, which grant aids the cost of carrying out energy improvements. The scheme applies to existing buildings only, and targets monitoring systems, heat recovery, CHP, modular and condensing boilers and building management systems in particular. Projects which involve renewable technologies only are excluded from the scheme. The maximum grant is 40 percent of the costs of improvements (excluding renewable technologies) up to a maximum of £100,000. *Contact: The Irish Energy Centre, Glasnevin, Dublin 9. Tel (01) 837 0101 Fax (01) 837 2848.*

FURTHER READING

- British Standards Institution. *A Designer's Manual for the Energy Efficient Refurbishment of Housing.* London, BSI, [198?]. 44 pp. Applications manual to accompany BS 8211 Part 1 BS Code of Practice on the Energy Efficient Refurbishment of Housing. Includes manual procedure for calculating annual energy consumption, and site checklist.

- Davidson, Paul. *Energy Conservation in Retrofit'.* Garston, Building Research Establishment, 1994.

- Friedemann & Johnson Consultants GmbH. *Insulation Measures for Retrofitting of Residential Buildings.* Berlin, Friedemann & Johnson - OPET for the European Commission, 1994. 25 pp. Free. Looks at technologies for thermal retrofitting of prefabricated panel-type multi-storey apartment buildings. Includes case studies. Available from: Energy Research Group, School of Architecture, UCD, Richview, Clonskeagh, Dublin 14. Tel (01) 269 2750 Fax (01) 283 8908.

- Friedemann & Johnson Consultants GmbH. *Retrofitting of Metering and Control Technology for Heating Systems in Residential Buildings.* Berlin, Friedemann & Johnson - OPET for the European Commission, 1994. 32 pp. Free. Focuses on multi-storey apartment buildings in central and eastern Europe. Includes case studies. Available from: Energy Research Group, School of Architecture, UCD, Richview, Clonskeagh, Dublin 14. Tel (01) 269 2750 Fax (01) 283 8908.

- *Living in the City : Architectural Ideas Competition for the Remodelling of Apartment Buildings.* Published by the Energy Research Group, University College Dublin, for the European Commission. Kinsale, Gandon Irish Art Books, 1996. Competition documentation (including refurbishment design guidelines), competition entries and jury reports.

- Royal Institute of the Architects of Ireland. *Guidelines for the Conservation of Buildings.* Dublin, RIAI, 1995. Free.

Section
B13

ENSURING GOOD PERFORMANCE

Limerick RTC, Limerick, Murray O' Laoire

An Energy Performance Assessment of 31 passive solar low energy buildings from the domestic and non-domestic sectors in the UK was completed in 1993 (Vaughan and Jones, 1994). The buildings were studied over an eight year period, and most worked well. The problems that did arise included: conflicting strategies; too much concentration on exotic devices and not enough attention to basics; failures of detailing; late omission of critical design elements; poor construction; misuse by occupants; and inadequate communication with users. None of these is very surprising. Problems occurring in conventional buildings can often be traced to the same sources.

Clarity of purpose and good communications are fundamental in the production of any successful building. In sustainable design, where some of the concepts and techniques are unfamiliar, they are critical.

I DESIGN AND SPECIFICATION

Conventional engineering design builds in tolerances and safety margins. In the relatively new field of sustainable design, where theory may not yet be supported by extensive experience in application, caution is even more advisable. Robust design solutions are preferable to finely balanced systems which depend on precise assumptions being correct.

Making systems more complex, so as to achieve greater flexibility in building response, will be counter-productive if it raises the burden of building management to unrealistic levels.

Conflicting strategies and failures of detailing are very much less likely if the fundamental design moves, and the principles underlying them, are clearly stated and agreed between all members of the design team. If this is done successfully, it is also less likely that later cost-trimming exercises will result in the elimination of some element that is critical to the effective performance of the building. The UK study reports how the omission of some internal doors, at a saving of £1250 Stg. on an extension project worth £32,000, undermined the entire heating and ventilation system.

Selection criteria for products and materials should be recorded. In the case of late substitution it will then be possible to check that the proposed alternative meets the original criteria.

2 CONSTRUCTION

Poor workmanship, whether caused by cost-cutting, carelessness or ignorance, will undermine even the best thought-out sustainable design strategy. Good communications and close site supervision are essential. If novel techniques or unusually exacting standards of workmanship and site management are critical to successful operation of the completed building, or to meet environmental objectives, the reasons must be explained.

3 THE USERS

If occupants open windows instead of trickle vents on sunny winter days, the building's energy performance will be compromised. Failure to separate cans and bottles from food waste in a canteen kitchen will frustrate re-cycling objectives. These are familiar enough situations. If a project incorporates more unusual features - daylight sensors or reed-beds, for example - users may be entirely at a loss. To some extent responsibility for the correct use of a building rests with building owners and managers, but a great deal lies also with the design team. Arriving at a realistic estimate of what can be expected from the occupants is particularly important in sustainable design.

In some cases, lack of user co-operation can be overcome by the use of automatic controls, but this costs more and there is the risk of the controls malfunctioning. Systems are more likely to work well if they are simple and self-explanatory. A bank of light switches whose layout corresponds clearly with the layout of the light fittings will encourage selective use of lighting.

The operating instructions given to owner or developer at hand-over could well be supplemented by a 'users manual' for tenants or employees. Employees who are used to centralised control systems may be reluctant to 'tamper' with the thermostatic radiator valve in their offices. If it is a mixed control system, with some automation and some provision for personal intervention, the potential for confusion is increased. In the case of a retrofit project it is particularly important to keep occupants informed, set realistic energy saving targets and time scales, monitor performance and provide good feedback to everyone involved.

It is important that the instructions for the owner/occupier highlight any aspect of the building's operation that would be compromised by additions such as internal partitions, or by changes introduced in the course of routine maintenance.

4   CONTROLS

If a passive solar building is to achieve energy savings it is important that the conventional systems operate only when needed, and then as efficiently as possible. Building services installations are designed on the basis of annual weather statistics. Fine-tuning their performance depends on being able to respond to actual conditions, inside and outside the building.

Thermostats, programmable timers, and optimum start controls are familiar. Weather compensation controls adjust the flow temperature in a heating circuit in response to changes in external temperature; boiler sequence controls manage multiple-boiler installations for maximum efficiency over varying demand cycles. In buildings of complex or sophisticated daylight design, particularly those with exterior adjustable daylighting devices, integrated automatic lighting control systems are probably essential.

A Building Research Establishment (BRE) study of the reasons for poor performance of automatic lighting control systems in some office buildings found that the most highly sophisticated were not always the most successful (Slater, 1991). Simple systems tended to be more robust. Misunderstandings about control strategies, lack of attention to detail, and unreal assumptions about human behaviour caused sub-optimal performance. Initial weaknesses in design and installation were compounded by building managers' lack of time or skills, and few systems gave managers the kind of feedback they needed to improve performance. It is probably fair to say that the same kinds of problems occur with complex control systems for other services.

A building energy management system (BEMS) can synchronise the performance of all the climate control systems in the building - daylighting and artificial lighting, heating, cooling and ventilation - as conditions change indoors and out. It can be a powerful tool for optimising energy use and equipment maintenance schedules, but adequate time must be allocated to monitoring the information it provides, and acting on it. Many existing systems are poorly used, for the reasons revealed by the BRE study, with the result that opportunities for energy and cost savings are lost. Well applied BEMS can be very effective. The Copthorne Hotel, Devon cut its 1988 annual energy consumption of 5,762,380 kWh by 53 percent over a four year period. This was achieved by modest capital expenditure of £19,200 on water heaters, energy efficient lamps, and controls, combined with committed energy management (*Energy Efficiency in Hotels,* 1995).

Any automatic control system should be designed so that it is possible to over-ride it when necessary. It is important also that the occupants feel that they have some control over conditions in their workspace. 'Autocratic' control systems which appear to switch things on and off in an arbitrary way will irritate users, and may be sabotaged or disconnected.

5   MONITORING AND TARGETING

The foundation of effective energy management is the creation of a system of monitoring and targeting. This equips building owners or managers with the information, and the motivation, to attain lower levels of energy consumption.

Monitoring should aim to measure energy consumption and operating costs, and register changes in either. Setting realistic targets and checking actual performance will help to ensure that all systems are maintained in optimum working condition. If targets are not being met, remedial action can be taken. If they are being met without undue effort, the targets can be raised.

Build so that you can monitor afterwards. The main elements of a monitoring and targeting system are:

5.1   Metering

Sub-metering allows detailed energy monitoring. Separate meters should be provided in areas where high energy consumption is expected, or if the building is likely to accommodate a number of independent groups.

5.2   Building Operation and Maintenance Manuals

These should be designed and compiled with the energy manager in mind. Weather data used in the design should be included, together with a full set of drawings and schematics of all energy using plant and equipment, clearly indicating power ratings, fuel types, and design conditions for each area of the building. The estimate of energy consumption arrived at during the design process should be handed over to the building occupier as an initial energy target.

5.3   Building Energy Management System (BEMS)

A description of the BEMS' capabilities should include comprehensive instructions on how to monitor energy consumption, log results, and carry out analyses. A BEMS offers the advantage that data from all systems and spaces in the building can be collected with ease, and targets set, from a single personal computer.

6   MAINTENANCE

Planned preventative maintenance (PPM), particularly of services, can reduce running costs by up to 15 percent, and double or treble the life of plant and equipment. It also provides higher quality conditions inside the buildings and reduces pollutant emissions outside it.

The design team can encourage good maintenance by designing for durability, and providing easy access to service runs and spaces. If at all possible, talk to the people who will be responsible for building management and maintenance at an early stage in the design process. Hand-over information should give thorough guidance on how the building operates and how it should be run.

7   FEEDBACK

Because of the particular difficulties of sustainable design, and the shortage of solid design data, it is more necessary than ever to monitor building performance and get user feedback. Data collected over a number of years will inform designers about what works and what does not. Implementation of routine feedback procedures by design practices would generate a fund of information on productive and practicable design strategies.

FURTHER READING

- U.K. Department of the Environment. *Environmental Action Guide for Building and Purchasing Managers*. London, HMSO, 1991. 34 pp. £5.50 Stg. Supplemented by Advisory Notes on implementation.

- UK. Department of the Environment. Energy Efficiency Office. *Energy Efficiency in New Housing: Detailing for Designers and Building Professionals. Good Practice Guides Nos. 93 - 97.* London, HMSO, 1993-95. Guide 93 Key detailing principles; Guide 94 Ground floors; Guide 95 External cavity walls; Guide 96 Windows and external doors; Guide 97 Pitched roofs. A useful series of 8 - 29 page publications, well-illustrated, highlighting areas of risk, with advice on specification, buildability and site supervision.

- Sadgrove, Kit. *The Green Manager's Handbook*. Aldershot, Gower Publishing Ltd., 1992. 274 pp. £35 Stg. Designed to help business people put sustainable principles into practice. Includes case histories, specimen policies and procedures. Covers environmental audits, energy management, developing green products, waste management, employees, public relations, finance and accounting.

- Brand, Stewart. *How Buildings Learn: What Happens After they are Built*. London, Viking, 1994.

GREEN PROJECT CHECKLIST

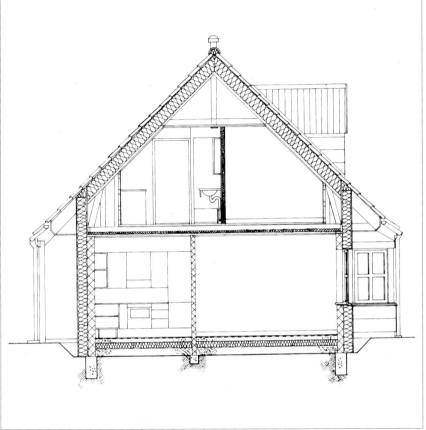

*Section through a CLEAR house (low **C**ost **L**ow **E**nergy, **A**llergy and **R**adon minimizing) Architects: Lars Højensgårds Tegnestue*

C.L.E.A.R. House.
Sustainable features include:
Low embodied energy in materials;
Passive Solar Gain;
Air-tight construction;
Passive fresh air-ventilation;
External insulation with high internal thermal mass to retain heat;
Vapour-permeable construction to avoid condensation;
Water-conserving sanitary and kitchen appliances;
Radon barrier at floor level.

BRIEFING

Brief client on sustainable options.
Agrêe outline sustainable objectives with client and design team.

* Review, refine, and agree as project proceeds.

SITE APPRAISAL

Encourage site location choices which minimise environmental impact and social costs, and the need for transport or new infrastructure.

Assess site potential: microclimate, slope, orientation, shelter, sunlight, daylight, views, soil, vegetation, water, recyclable materials for building or landscaping, renewable energies, existing structures, historical, cultural or wildlife features.

Assess site problems: geology, pollution, contamination, exposure, density, noise, hazards, radon, overshadowing.

* Evaluate environmental implications.

OUTLINE PROPOSALS

Locate building so as to limit impact on site; minimise area of hard landscape; protect natural and cultural assets.

Landscape site to create shelter from wind, noise, air pollution; preserve or improve soil, water resources, wildlife, vegetation.

Re-use existing structures where possible.

Plan siting, orientation and massing of buildings to exploit shelter, solar gain, daylight, natural ventilation.

Incorporate appropriate renewable energies: passive solar, active solar, hydro, wind, photovoltaics, biomass.

- Evaluate local and global impact.

SCHEME DESIGN

Establish target comfort conditions and tolerances; zone spaces and activities in terms of required indoor climate conditions.

Use plan, section and fenestration to exploit solar gain, daylight, sunlight, natural ventilation; take account of external air pollution and noise.

Design structure and envelope to exploit thermal mass if appropriate.

Design envelope to prevent overheating and to limit heat loss.

Incorporate 'active' renewable energy systems as appropriate.

Size conventional building services to take account of reduced load. Consider heat recovery; combined heat and power. Incorporate water conserving strategies.

Plan for climate-responsive control systems.

Consider waste generation, recycling and disposal.

Consider sustainability of materials to be used.

- Review building performance: comfort, health, energy consumption, operating costs, environmental impact, regulations.

DETAIL DESIGN

Detail envelope to eliminate cold bridges, interstitial condensation and infiltration; detail for durability.

Balance heat and light transmission characteristics of glazing; provide insulation and shading where necessary.

Fine-tune passive solar heating, daylighting and natural ventilation strategies.

Identify characteristics of finishes needed to support passive solar strategies: conductivity, colour and reflectance, acoustic properties.

Specify materials which are safe, durable and/or recyclable; use recycled materials where possible, give preference to materials from sustainable resources, manufactured by clean, low-energy processes and produced close to the site.

Specify energy efficient and low-emission fuels, appliances and fittings for conventional heating, cooling, ventilation and lighting systems.

Specify water-conserving sanitary and domestic fittings.

Plan reduction, recycling, disposal of wastes.

Specify energy-efficient office equipment and domestic appliances if this is within design team control.

Assess or agree realistic maintenance schedules.

Design user-friendly control and monitoring systems.

- Review design in relation to sustainable objectives.

PRODUCTION INFORMATION

Revise standard specification clauses to incorporate sustainable issues as appropriate.

Ensure that unfamiliar techniques, systems or details are clearly explained in drawings and specification.

TENDER ACTION

Include sustainable objectives in invitation to tender. Specify any special requirements as to building performance, commissioning tests, site practices.

Evaluate ability of contractors to implement any non-conventional techniques or design features, and to meet standards of workmanship required to achieve target building performance.

CONSTRUCTION

Ensure that construction team are informed of sustainable objectives and requirements.

Enforce clauses on materials, workmanship, sustainable site practices.

HAND-OVER

Consider independent energy or environmental certification of building.

Ensure that all systems are commissioned and tested to conform to performance specifications.

Provide full operating and maintenance instructions for owner/occupier, building manager and users. Include information on performance monitoring and targets.

FEEDBACK

Arrange for feedback from monitoring.

Arrange independent assessment of performance/user satisfaction after some years' use. Incorporate lessons in subsequent projects.

House at Doolin. Grafton Architects.

PART
C

EVALUATING DESIGN PROPOSALS

In the course of any project the design team is constantly trying to assess the likely performance of the building. For a team new to sustainable issues there is the added complication of having to make judgements in areas of which its members have little experience.

How will the building rate in terms of its energy consumption and its impact on the environment? Will conditions inside the building remain within acceptable limits for comfort? Will the investment in sustainable strategies bring a reasonable financial return? Is it worthwhile upgrading an existing building, or would the client be better advised to sell or demolish, and start afresh? Will the building be more, or less, marketable than a conventional building? Will it comply with the Regulations?

This Part of the manual covers tools, techniques and services which can provide some support to design teams confronting these issues. Rules of thumb, often the most useful aids in the early stages of any design process, are not included here, but in the Sections of Part B to which they apply.

TOOLS FOR DESIGN AND EVALUATION

RADIANCE

There are now available many tools for use in the design of sustainable buildings. This Section covers some of the general implications of using design and evaluation tools, and highlights for each design stage at least one tool that looks at heating, ventilation and/or daylighting. (The particular tools listed are chosen as representative of their kind. Inclusion or omission carries no implication as to quality.)

Some of the CAD packages used by architects can show the pattern of shadows thrown by the sun from a specified position, but they provide no information on levels of daylight or of solar radiation. Services engineers, on the other hand, routinely use software design tools, such as *Cymap* and *Hevacomp* , to calculate thermal, lighting and energy balances. None really provide sufficient speed and flexibility in answering the full range of questions which arise for architects during the sketch design stage, but they do make it possible to make approximate evaluations of alternative sketch proposals. This would once have been impracticable because of the calculation time involved.

EU funded work on the integration of CAD systems and computer-based design and evaluation tools has advanced a considerable distance. The intention is to produce a network that, for practical purposes, would operate as a single, designer-friendly package. (Some of the tools listed in this Section can be linked to CAD systems. Where this is the case, it is stated in the description.) Meanwhile, architects should ask their services consultants what software they have and what its capabilities are. Early collaboration and feedback can result in more effective solutions.

Traditional scale models should not be dismissed. They are easy to manipulate at the early design stages, their workings and limitations are clearly evident at all times, and they allow the designer to make quick visual and intuitive judgements of what is happening.

Information Requirements

Data requirements vary widely from one tool to another, depending on the level and complexity of the analysis. Tools intended for use early in the design process, when information about the building itself is very limited, are generally referred to as 'design tools'. They cannot predict performance, but can indicate the strategic implications of different design proposals. The most commonly used building-services software tools are based on steady-state conditions. They are useful for comparing options, or for examining worst case conditions, at any design stage. Predicting likely performance in use, however, demands a dynamic 'evaluation tool' to simulate the response of the building to changes in internal and external conditions over time. This can involve hour-by-hour simulation of building performance, and will probably require a full building description and extensive meteorological data.

Accuracy of Results

All tools, whether manual or computer-based, are based on assumptions about the phenomenon being analysed. This is unavoidable, because arriving at exact and universally valid descriptions is impossible. Always bear this in mind when interpreting their results.

Computing Consultancy Services

Some of the computer-based tools are relatively inexpensive and can operate on the kind of equipment commonly available in architectural and engineering practices. The more advanced systems lie beyond the scope of most practices, or would be needed so rarely that the purchase and training costs would be uneconomic. Both the Dublin Institute of Technology, and the Energy Research Group, University College Dublin, offer computer simulation services to architects and services engineers. *Contact: Paul Kenny, Energy Research Group, School of Architecture, University College Dublin, Richview, Clonskeagh, Dublin 14. Tel (01) 269 2750 Fax (01) 283 8908 or Ken Beattie, Dublin Institute of Technology, Bolton Street, Dublin 1. Tel (01) 402 3822 Fax (01) 402 3999.*

1   TOOLS FOR SITE ASSESSMENT

CYLINDRICAL SUNPATH DIAGRAM: A graphic tool, used with site plans and sections, to plot obstructions such as hills, buildings and trees and establish when sunlight can reach the site. This information can be used for sunlight penetration studies and for heat gain calculations. (The technique is explained in Appendix 2.)

SCALE MODELS: If the pattern of site obstructions is complex, a site model used with a heliodon may be the quickest way of establishing solar access. (With small scale models the accuracy of sun movements can be taken to be to the nearest half hour.) Scale models can be used later in the design process to study shadowing in relation to the new building.

Using a scale model of the site and its surrounding area, and a fan which generates a laminar flow of air, an approximate picture of the pattern of wind exposure and shelter on an urban or suburban site can be established. A thin layer of semolina is sprinkled over the site and the fan used to simulate wind from prevailing wind directions. The semolina will form drifts in sheltered pockets. The same technique can be used later in the design process to study the wind effect of the new building/s.

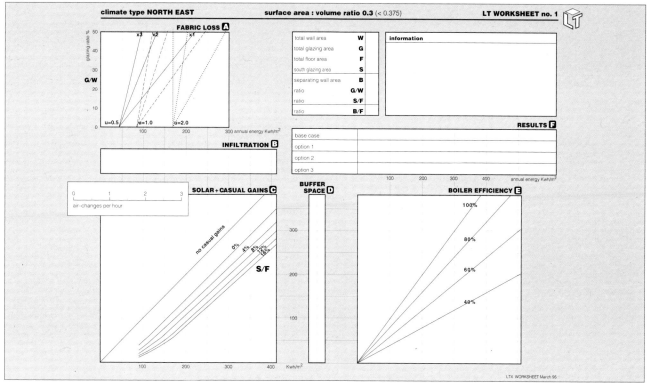

L.T. METHOD

2   TOOLS FOR THE EARLY DESIGN STAGE

LT METHOD 2.0   A manual technique for evaluating the energy implications of building form and glazing ratios in non-domestic buildings at the sketch design stage. The objective is to establish the optimum balance between heating, cooling and lighting, taking solar gain, heat loss and daylighting into account. Atria and sunspaces are covered. The technique requires only the use of pencil, calculator and LT Worksheets, and the publication includes worked examples. *Available from: Building Research Establishment, Garston, Watford, Herst, WD2 7JR, United Kingdom. Tel: +44.1923-664 444 Fax: +44.1923-664 400. Price: £6.00 Stg. incl. post and packaging.*

UNICALC

UNICALC: A software tool, developed in Ireland, for evaluating performance in relation to Part L of the Building Regulations. The program features a database of building materials from which to build each construction element, layer by layer; calculation of U-values in accordance with the Building Regulations; condensation risk analysis in accordance with BS 5250 1989. (For PC, Windows 3.1 or later versions.) *Available from: ERI Ltd, P.O. Box 3120, Dublin 16. Tel: 01-4970133 Fax: 01-4970383. Price: IR£ 199 + VAT.*

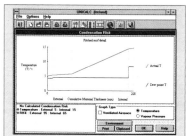

UNICALC

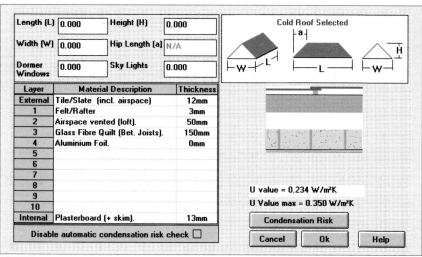

UNICALC

PASSPORT: A software tool for predicting solar and internal gains for passive solar residential buildings. It takes account of interactions between different rooms within the building and incorporates a database of materials and glazing characteristics. (For PC/MS-DOS, 3.0 or later versions.) *Available from: Energy Research Group, School of Architecture, University College Dublin. Tel (01) 269 2750 Fax (01) 1 283 8908. Price: IR£ 80.*

BREVENT: A software tool for predicting ventilation rates in dwellings. It is a single room model, based on a set of equations describing windows, openings (trickle vents, air bricks, etc.) extractors, combustion appliances and passive stack ventilation devices. (For PC / MS-DOS.) *Available from: Building Research Establishment, Garston, Watford, Herst, WD2 7JR, United Kingdom. Tel: +44.1923-664 444 Fax: +44.1923-664 400. Price £400 stg*

SCALE MODELS: A scale model makes an excellent daylight design tool. Provided that it is viewed under natural lighting conditions identical to those on the site, and its surfaces have the correct reflectances, luminances and illuminances will reach the same values in the model as they will in reality. Placed on a heliodon, the model can be used to assess sunlight penetration at different times of the day and the year. Wind-tunnel testing of models - including surrounding buildings and streets - can simulate new conditions in large projects, or among groups of high buildings. Detailed results, for all wind directions, can greatly influence design of the envelope, location of entrances, flues, ventilation, fire and wind loading. The nearest test facilities are in the UK.

3 TOOLS FOR THE INTERMEDIATE DESIGN STAGE

By this stage in the design process more detailed information about the building is available. Decisions on building fabric, insulation levels and glazing characteristics, and on the type of heating and lighting systems to be used, will have been taken.

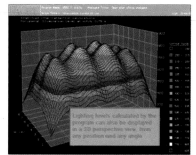

INTERFACET

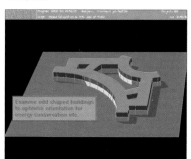

INTERFACET

BRE DAYLIGHT PROTRACTORS: Tools for establishing, from drawings, sky component and externally reflected component for use in daylight factor calculations. Set includes literature and protractor set, nos. 1 - 10, for vertical, horizontal and sloped glazing. *Available from: Building Research Establishment, Garston, Watford, Herst WD2 7JR, United Kingdom. Tel: +44.1923-664 444 Fax: +44.1923-664 400. . Price: £20 Stg. Daylight Protractor No. 2 (for vertical glazing) is available separately at £3 Stg.*

INTERFACET: Software packages useful to both architect and engineer. The set includes packages for: heat loss and condensation in composite elements; steady state design heat loss of a building of any shape or orientation; heat gains and internal temperatures in air conditioned buildings (operating parameters for each room can be set individually); lighting design and simulation; room acoustics; lifts; pipe and ductwork sizing; and electrical distribution. A system simulation package calculates annual energy consumption of a HVAC system and the annual electrical consumption for lighting and equipment, from schedules and levels of use defined by the user.

Each module can be purchased and used separately, but all can exchange files and can be linked with MicroStation CAD. Information can be scanned from MicroStation (.dgn) and AutoCAD (.dwg) and used to predict shading, airflows, daylighting, artificial lighting and thermal behaviour. (For PC Windows and UNIX). *Available from: FACET Ltd, Marlborough House, Upper Marlborough Road, St. Albans, Hertfordshire AL1 3UT, United Kingdom. Tel: +44.1727-850 830 Fax: +44.181-784 5700 Price: from £1,500 Stg per module, with reductions for multiple purchases.*

BREEZE: A program for predicting ventilation and air flows in complex multi-celled buildings, both new and refurbished. (For PC / MS-DOS) *Available from: Building Research Establishment, Garston, Watford, Herst WD2 7JR, United Kingdom. Tel: +44.1923-664 444 Fax: +44.1923-664 400. Price: £450 Stg.*

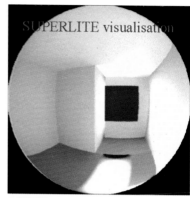

SUPERLITE

SUPERLITE: A program for predicting interior daylight illuminances in complex spaces under a variety of sun and sky conditions. The model can accommodate most standard window or skylight fenestration systems, internal solid or glazed partitions, interior and exterior obstructions, and differing glazing types. The software can import standard CAD dxf format files. (For PC / MS-DOS)

Like RADIANCE (see below), SUPERLITE is part of ADELINE, an assembly of tools which includes SCRIBE-MODELLER as a CAD interface, and connects with energy simulation tools (tsbi3, SUNCODE, DOE 2 and TRNSYS) using SUPERLINK, to assess the energy implications of lighting proposals. *Available from: Hans Erhorn, Fraunhofer-Institut fur Bauphysik, Nobelstr. 12, D-70569 Stuttgart, Germany.: Price: ADELINE $400.*

4   ADVANCED DESIGN / EVALUATION TOOLS

The tools described in this section are highly sophisticated, and expensive to run. They require an experienced operator and very detailed design information. They also need greater than average computer power. At present it is unlikely that their use will be justified in normal circumstances, but they are often appropriate for the analysis of complex component design, or where a new technique is being used and there exists no previous basis for comparison.

RADIANCE: A simulation system which uses ray-tracing techniques to predict lighting levels in and the appearance of daylit and artificially lit spaces. The quality and accuracy of the photo-realistic image produced is very high. The image may be analysed, displayed and manipulated within the package, or converted to other popular image file formats to produce hard copy. Minimum recommended configuration is 8 Mbytes of RAM, 16 Mbytes of free disk space, and an 8-bit color display. A fast processor and floating point support are strongly recommended. The software runs on most UNIX systems and most of the programs will run unmodified on non-UNIX systems. It can import CAD files. *Available as part of the ADELINE Software package (see SUPERLITE above) from: Hans Erhorn, Fraunhofer-Institut fur, Bauphysik, Nobelstr. 12, D-70569 Stuttgart, Germany . RADIANCE may also be downloaded from one of the two "official" RADIANCE ftp sites:* Σ *hobbes.lbl.gov* Σ *nestor.epfl.ch (at /pub/unix/radiance) There is no charge for the software and documentation when downloaded via the network.*

RADIANCE

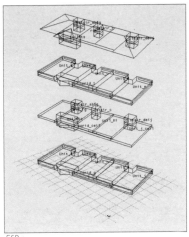
ESP-r

ESP-r: A dynamic thermal simulation system for building fabric, mass flow, and plant systems examined separately or in combination. Design problems can be specified in terms of building geometry, opaque and transparent construction materials, surface finishes, occupancy, lighting schemes, and small power loads - with superimposed events to represent windows being opened, shades moved and electric lights being switched on or off. To minimise input workload, users are offered access to on-line databases of construction materials, plant components, profile prototypes, optical properties, pressure coefficients and climatic sequences. (For UNIX. The most common user interface is via the X Window libraries (X11 V5). It is also possible to run ESP-r under Open Windows. ESP-r can import CAD files. *Training courses and the source code for ESP-r are available from: Energy Systems Research Unit, Energy Systems Division University of Strathclyde, 75 Montrose Street Glasgow G1 1XJ, SCOTLAND. Tel:+44 141 552 4400 Fax: +44 141 552 8513. Price: Free to research users. For professional use contact the University of Strathclyde.*

DOE-2: A set of programs for analysing energy consumption in buildings. The programs can calculate the heating and cooling loads for each space for each hour of a year; simulate the operation and response of control systems; model oil, gas or solar equipment for heating, cooling, and power; and compute the life-cycle costs of building operation. A user-oriented language facilitates the description of building geometry, central plant, HVAC systems, occupancy, equipment, lighting schedules, and other parameters. (For DOS/Windows 3.1, Windows NT, OS/2, Macintosh, ULTRIX 4.1, AIX 3.2, NeXTStep 3.x, VMS and for the SUN Sparc.) *Further information from: Andre Dewint, Alphi Pi s.a., rue de Livourne 103/12, B-1050 Bruxelles, Belgium. Tel: +32.2-649 8359 Fax: +32.3-649 9437. Price $1,200 - 1,700.*

FLUENT: A fluid dynamics package for analysing air flow in and around buildings. It provides information on flow characteristics such as pressure loss, flow distribution and mixing rates, and predicts fluid flow, heat and mass transfer and related phenomena. It can import CAD files. (For PC and UNIX machines, but requires more than 24 Mb RAM). *Available From: Fluent Europe Ltd., Hutton's Buildings, 146 West Street, Sheffield, S1 4ES, UK. Tel: +44.114-281 8888 Fax: +44.114-281 8818. Price: PC perpetual licence, incl. free training, £14,000 Stg. UNIX annual licence, incl. free training, technical support and updates, £13,750 Stg.*

FURTHER READING

- Kenny, Paul and J. Owen Lewis, Editors. *Tools and Techniques for the Design and Evaluation of Energy Efficient Buildings.* Dublin, UCD - OPET for the European Commission, 1996. 20 pp. Free. Available from: Energy Research Group, School of Architecture, UCD, Richview, Clonskeagh, Dublin 14. Tel (01) 269 2750 Fax (01) 283 8908. Also available on THERMIE World Wide Web site (http://erg.ucd.ie/opethermie).

AUDITS, ASSESSMENTS AND CERTIFICATION

Distinctions must be made between audits, assessments and certification. An energy audit, as its name suggests, measures the energy performance of a building. A building with a good energy performance is likely to have less environmental impact than a building with a poor one but, apart from measuring indoor air temperatures, an energy audit makes no judgement about environmental issues.

An environmental assessment covers a wide range of issues, which overlap with those covered by an Environmental Impact Statement carried out under the EC (Environmental Impact Assessment) Regulations. An Environmental Impact Statement focuses on the local and regional impact of the building and of the processes carried out in it. An environmental assessment of the building assesses energy performance, health and comfort inside the building, and its local and global impact.

An energy audit or an environmental assessment may be carried out by the design team or by an independent consultant. Energy or environmental certification, on the other hand, must be carried out by an independent consultant or agency. A standardised procedure is used to measure the predicted or actual performance of the building against a norm for its building type, and the rating is documented by the issue of a certificate.

Ratings of the energy or environmental performance of buildings can provide useful feedback during the design process and increase the marketability of the completed building. This Section reviews some of the options available.

1   ENERGY AUDITS FOR EXISTING BUILDINGS

The purpose of an energy audit is to identify opportunities for cost-effective energy savings. It is usually undertaken as a prelude to retrofitting, or as part of a survey prior to purchase. In the case of a retrofit, the design team, as a first step, can carry out a check using the Normalised Performance Indicator procedure described in Appendix 6. This will provide a rough indication as to how the building performs compared to others of its type, and whether an energy audit is advisable. Energy audits are carried out at two levels. In many cases a 'concise energy survey' will be adequate. However, if performance is very poor, or the project very complex, a 'comprehensive energy survey' may be necessary.

The Energy Audit Grants Scheme (EAGS) operated by the Irish Energy Centre provides grant assistance to organisations engaging independent consultants to carry out energy audits. A grant of up to 40 percent of the cost, excluding VAT, is available up to a maximum of £5,000. The scheme is open to industry, the commercial sector and institutions. A list of persons and organisations who provide energy audit services is available from the Centre. Typical costs for energy surveys, as shown in EAGS documentation, are shown here. *Contact: The Irish Energy Centre, Glasnevin, Dublin 9. Tel (01) 837 0101 Fax (01) 837 2848.*

Annual Energy Bill	Survey Guide Costs
Less than £10,000	A walk through survey may be considered appropriate to a maximum of grant of £500
£10,000 to £50,000	8 to 5% of annual energy bill
£50,000 to £500,000	5 to 3% of annual energy bill
More than £500,000	3 to 1% of annual energy bill

The Irish Energy Centre also operates the Energy Efficiency Investment Support Scheme, which grant aids the cost of carrying out energy improvements. (see B.12.8)

2   ENERGY ASSESSMENT AT THE DESIGN STAGE

Evaluating the likely energy performance of a building is an iterative procedure, carried out by the design team as the design progresses, and feeding back into the decision making process. The extent of evaluation will depend on the stage that the design is at, the complexity of the project, and the time and money available.

In the early stages simple manual calculations of heat losses, internal gains, solar gains and daylighting performance may be sufficient. The LT Method (see C.1.2), can provide a useful comparison of alternatives at the sketch design stage. As proposals become more detailed, software tools of the kind listed in Section C.1 can be useful.

It is anticipated that the Revised Building Regulations will include a manual procedure for calculating a 'Heat Energy Rating' for dwellings.

3   ENERGY CERTIFICATION

The only energy certification system in Ireland at present is the Benchmark system (NICER) operated by National Irish Centre for Energy Rating Ltd. This is a commercial service aimed at the residential buildings market. Construction, orientation, thermal mass, solar and conventional heating are incorporated in the model, which assesses energy use (in kWh/m^2) and CO_2 production under Irish weather conditions. The model can be applied to an existing building or at the design stage, and assesses performance under dynamic rather than steady-state conditions. A rating for a typical house costs £150 + VAT. *Contact: N.I.C.E.R., 3 Bushfield Place, Dublin 4. Tel. (01) 497 0133 Fax (01) 497 0383.*

4   ENVIRONMENTAL CERTIFICATION

At present there is no nationally approved environmental certification system operating in Ireland. Plans for an all-Ireland system based on the BREEAM scheme are under discussion. BREEAM is an environmental quality rating system for buildings, developed in the UK by the Building Research Establishment and The ECD Partnership. It is carried out by licensed assessors and results in the issue of a BRE-backed certificate. It is currently being applied to some 75 percent of new office development in the UK, and has been used for a small number of commercial buildings in Ireland. *Contact: Energy Research Group, School of Architecture, University College Dublin. Tel (01) 269 2750 Fax (01) 283 8908.*

5   ENVIRONMENTAL ASSESSMENT

A design team can use BREEAM procedures to carry out its own environmental assessment during the design stage. This course of action has limitations. Each issue covered by BREEAM can be assessed separately, but it is not possible either to arrive at an overall rating for the project, or to compare the building with BREEAM rated buildings of the same type. The information necessary for that part of the process is restricted to agencies or consultancies licensed to issue BREEAM certificates. However, it does provide targets and allows the design team to assess performance against standardised scales for a range of headings.

The BREEAM system is fairly conservative. Assessment covers only issues for which evidence on environmental consequences is strong, performance criteria can be well defined, and assessment at the design stage is feasible. Different versions of the procedure - for old and new office buildings, new homes, shopping centres and hypermarkets - are available.

Points are awarded for the inclusion of design features which are environment-friendly. Credit is given, for example, to a design predicted to produce less CO_2 per square metre of serviced floor area than a typical new building of the same type. The size of the credit earned under this heading depends on the magnitude of CO_2 savings. Assessment headings are listed below.

GLOBAL ISSUES :	CO_2 emissions acid rain ozone depletion due to CFCs, HCFCs and Halons natural resources and recycled materials storage of recyclable materials
LOCAL ISSUES :	legionnaires' disease from wet cooling towers local wind effects noise overshadowing of other buildings and land water economy ecological value of the site cyclists' facilities
INDOOR ISSUES :	legionnaires' disease from domestic hot water systems ventilation, passive smoking and humidity hazardous materials lighting thermal comfort and overheating indoor noise

For copies of BREEAM publications contact: BRE Bookshop, Building Research Establishment, Garston, Watford, WD2 7JR. Tel. +44 .1923-664444.

Section
C3

CALCULATING PAYBACK : LIFE CYCLE COST ANALYSIS

Life cycle costs are a significant factor in investment decisions. This Section is intended to give the reader some understanding of the principles and the limitations of life cycle costing, particularly as they relate to sustainable design. The examples presented are relatively simple. More complex and sophisticated methods do exist, but the techniques described here are those which would be applied to most everyday situations.

The life cycle cost of a building is the total cost over its operating life. It includes the initial acquisition costs, plus subsequent running and maintenance costs. In most buildings post-construction costs significantly exceed initial capital costs, and the impact of poor balancing of capital and running costs at the design stage is felt throughout the entire life of the building. One of the classic life cycle cost diagrams shows an iceberg, the visible part representing capital costs and the much greater part under the surface the occupancy costs (Flanagan and Norman, 1983).

It is not easy to generalise about life cycle costs. Tax regime, climate, building use and other issues play a part, and each situation must be considered on its merits. What makes sense for a pensioner on a fixed income may be inappropriate for someone on a heavily taxed inflating income. What is valid for one region may not apply to another. If degree days figures vary across the country, as they do, the economics of additional insulation must vary also.

Conventional life cycle cost techniques focus on the long-term financial implications of design decisions. They will not necessarily produce results that support environmentally justifiable investment in sustainable technology. A life cycle cost comparison of different heating systems will examine the costs of purchasing and installing plant, the consumption rates and prices of alternative fuels, the predicted life of the equipment, and the cost of maintenance. This is somewhat more likely to produce a sustainable design decision than a comparison of capital costs alone. But, what will not have been measured at any stage in the process are the 'external' costs - the total primary energy involved in electricity generation, the costs of ill-health caused by pollution, or the financial consequences of CO_2 related climate change.

The information generated by a life cycle cost exercise provides just one of the factors to be weighed. The client considering investment implications may be thinking also of enhanced property or rental value, reliability, improved working conditions or increases in productivity. The designer needs to be in a position to point out the implications, good or bad, for sustainability.

Life cycle costing techniques are equally relevant for new buildings and for the retro-fitting of existing buildings. In a low energy building many of the energy saving features are interdependent, so assessment of overall performance, rather than of individual measures, is essential.

Capital Cost

Occupancy Cost

I LIFE CYCLE COMPARISON TECHNIQUES

I.I The Payback Method

A recent study of a combined heat and power (CHP) installation for a major hotel in Dublin showed that for an investment of about IR£ 135,000, savings of over IR£ 55,000 per annum were achieved. This represented a *payback* period of just over 2.4 years; that is, a period of 2.4 years to recover the initial investment, ignoring differences in money values caused by interest rates and inflation. Put another way, there was a return on the investment of 40.7 percent, excellent by any standards. This is a simple technique, but in any but the most basic situations - comparing the cost of a once-off initial investment with the anticipated annual saving resulting from that investment, for example - may give misleading results.

$$\text{Payback Years} = \frac{\text{Capital costs}}{\text{Annual savings}}$$

I.2 Discounting

To compare the merits of a low energy compact fluorescent lamp, which lasts 10,000 hours and uses 23 watts/hr, with a standard incandescent lamp, which uses 100 watts and requires replacement every 1,000 hours, we need a method of comparing the value of money now and in the future. The stream of payments in both situations must be brought to the same base to be validly compared. This involves considering two separate but linked factors, interest rates and inflation, neither of which can be predicted with any certainty over a long period.

During the 1970s, when inflation was higher than interest rates, the real rate of return on a deposit account was negative. With inflation at 30 percent and the interest rate at 20 percent, an investment of IR£100 would have produced IR£120 at the end of one year. But inflation during the same period meant that you would then need IR£130 to purchase what you could have bought for IR£ 100 the year before. In real terms, the investment had diminished to 92 percent of its original value, a real return of minus 8 percent. In 1995, with inflation at around 2.5 percent, and interest rates typically at 7 to 8 percent, more logical economics apply. A positive real rate of return is achievable, even after paying tax on deposit interest.

This element in life cycle cost comparisons is dealt with by introducing a 'discount rate' into the calculations. The discount rate varies, depending on the relationship between inflation and interest rates, but currently a rate of from 3 to 5 percent is used for most purposes.

For periods in excess of one year the discount is calculated at a compound rate, using the formula for the Present Value (PV) of IR£1 to be received in n year's time at y% discount rate:

$$PV = \frac{1}{(1 + y)^n}$$

For example, the present requirement for IR£100 to be available in ten year's time, at a 3% discount rate is:

$$PV = \frac{£100}{(1 + 0.03)^{10}} = £74.41$$

I.3 Calculating the Current Value of a Regularly Recurring Cost

Another commonly used formula is an extension of the basic principles of discounting. To establish the present value of an annually recurring item (PVA), say a cleaning cost of IR£ 1,000, it is not necessary to calculate the discounted value for each year and add them all together.

Instead the formula below can be used.

$$PVA = \sum_{n=1}^{n} \frac{1}{(1+y)^n}$$

For a 25 year period, with a 5% discount rate, the equation becomes

$$PVA = \sum_{1}^{25} \frac{£1,000}{(1+0.05)^{25}} = IR£\ 14,093$$

In other words, if you invest IR£ 14,093 now at a real return or discounting rate of 5 percent, you can deplete the account at the rate of IR£ 1,000 per annum plus inflation and the account will be fully and exactly depleted at the end of the 25 period.

2   WORKED EXAMPLE
DO LOW ENERGY BULBS REALLY PAY?

Using the following parameters, compare an incandescent light bulb with a low-energy compact fluorescent.

	Incandescent 100 watt IR£	Low Energy 23 watt IR£
Initial capital cost	0.70	14.00
Running costs at 1000 hours per annum and 7p per kw/hr	IR£ 7/annum	IR£ 1.61/annum
Life expectancy	1,000 hrs	10,000 hrs

This gives the following Life Cycle comparison for a ten year period:

Item			100 Watt IR£	23 Watt Long Life IR£
Initial Capital Cost			0.70	14.00
Replacement cost at the end of each year, discounted at 3% per annum; discounting factors				
Year	1	0.971		
	2	0.943		
	3	0.915		
	4	0.888		
	5	0.862		
	6	0.837		
	7	0.813		
	8	0.789		
	9	0.766		
	Total	7.784		
x IR£ 0.70			5.45	nil
Running costs over 10 years, discounted at 3% per annum; discounting factor:				
Years 1 to 9, as above	7.784			
Year 10	0.744			
	Total	8.528	x IR£ 7 59.70	x IR£ 1.61 13.73
Total Life Cycle Cost over 10 Years			**IR£ 65.85**	**IR£ 27.73**

On the basis of these specifications it is clear that the low energy bulb is a better investment. If its life expectancy was the same as the incandescent bulb, then the benefit would disappear and its discounted replacement cost each year would add 7.784 x IR£14 = IR£108.98 to its costs, bringing the overall total 10 year costs to IR£136.71. Similarly, if long life was achieved without any reduction in wattage, the additional running costs would add IR£45.97 (8.528 × IR£5.39) to give a total of IR£73.69. The low energy bulb needs both long life *and* low energy consumption to justify its selection solely on economic grounds.

One factor not taken into account in this comparison is the fact that the low-energy bulb will make a smaller contribution to heating the building during the winter. Over a six months heating season the difference in heat contributed by the low energy and incandescent bulbs is 77 watts × say 500 hours = 38.5 kW/hr. If this has to be supplied by an alternative source, again at 7p per kW/hr or IR£2.70 per annum, then the comparison changes again:

Item	100 Watts IR£	23 Watts IR£
Total previously	65.85	27.73
Additional heating costs years 1-10, discounted as before 8.528 × IR£2.70		23.02
Revised Total	**65.85**	**50.75**

The gap narrows, but the low energy bulb is still clearly the better option. In some buildings, the reduced contribution to heating will be of positive benefit, because it reduces the summer cooling load.

What none of the analyses show, because it is not factored into the calculations, is that installing a single low-energy compact fluorescent lamp also avoids the generation of three-quarters of a tonne of carbon dioxide and 8 Kg of sulphur dioxide over its working life (Browning and Romm, 1995). This is a case where the financial interests of the building owner and the good of the environment coincide.

3   MARGINAL COMPARISONS

Increasing investment in insulation produces a diminishing return. This is because doubling the insulation thickness does not halve the U value of the building element. Consider a roofing detail, where three options are under consideration: one with no insulation, one with 50 mm insulation and one with 100 mm insulation. The 50 mm insulation gives a return of 39.1 percent. The 100 mm insulation reduces the overall return to 27.4 percent, still a very good outcome.

Construction	U Value, say	Extra Cost per m²	Estimated Annual saving/m² (reduction in U value × IR£ 0.95)³	Return on Investment %	Payback period years
1. Basic Roof	2.60	-	-		
2. Basic roof with 50mm insulation	0.54 (i.e., 2.06 reduction)	IR£ 5.00	2.06 × IR£0.95= IR£1.96	39.1	2.56
3. Basic roof with 100mm insulation	0.30 (i.e. 2.30 reduction)	IR£8.00	2.30 × IR£0.95= IR£2.19	27.4	3.65

However, if this is looked at solely in terms of the investment in the additional 50 mm, the picture changes significantly. The return has dropped to 7.7 percent.

Construction	U Value, say	Extra Cost per m²	Estimated Annual saving/m² (reduction in U value × IR£ 0.95)³	Return on Invest-ment %	Payback period years
Increase 50mm to 100mm insulation (item 3 less item 2 above)	0.24	3.00	0.23	7.7	13.04

Marginal comparisons can have the reverse effect where retrofitting is involved. In the example below, single-glazed windows are to be replaced with double-glazed windows at an all-in cost of £200/m² of window area. The increased U value will reduce heating costs by IR£ 2.57 per m² of window per annum. The absolute cost will be:

Investment/m²	IR£ 200
Saving per m² per annum	IR£ 2.57
Payback period	77.8 years
Return on investment	1.29 percent

This is hardly worth considering on financial grounds alone. But if the windows need replacement anyway and the extra cost of double glazing is IR£ 30/m², then a different scenario emerges:

Additional investment/m²	IR£30
Saving per m² per annum	2.57
Payback period	11.67 years
Return on investment	8.57 percent

4   A NEGATIVE RETURN

Because increasing insulation does not produce a pro-rata reduction in U value, there comes a point where the economic return on additional insulation will be virtually nil. There eventually arises a situation where the energy required to manufacture, transport and install the additional insulation will be greater than the energy saving produced by the additional insulation over the life of the building.

5   ASSESSING THE RESULTS OF A LIFE CYCLE COSTING

It is possible to become over-concerned about variables and fine points of detail. Predicting the future is impossible, and the real purpose of the exercise is to make valid comparisons between different solutions. If a comparison shows options to be close in cost then it may be worthwhile to repeat the exercise using different parameters - a higher or lower discount rate, for example - to test the sensitivity of the options under different scenarios. This is particularly valid when you are comparing a single lump sum investment - new double glazing, for example - with a stream of payments in the future.

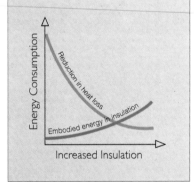
Energy consumption and insulation

FURTHER READING

- Flanagan, Roger and George Norman. *Life Cycle Costing for Construction*, London, Surveyor Publications for The Royal Institution of Chartered Surveyors, c. 1983. 128 pp. Out of print.

COMPLYING WITH REGULATIONS

A conscientious designer who wants to adopt sustainable strategies is faced with more dilemmas than is a colleague who is unconcerned about such issues. Take the Building Regulations as an example. The methods of compliance described in the Technical Guidance Documents to the Building Regulations are explicitly non-mandatory. A design team which is pursuing sustainable strategies will at times find that better results can be obtained by diverging from TGD methods. In that case, the safety net of "prima facie compliance with the requirements" of the Building Regulations will be missing. In the absence of a Building Regulations approvals system such as is found in almost every other EU Member State, the burden of proof, in the event of alleged non-compliance, will sometimes fall on the designer.

This may have varying practical consequences. The system of private sector enforcement of compliance, through the property conveyancing process, is erratic, and is ill-equipped to make judgements on compliance for anything out of the ordinary. On the other hand, there will usually be a material reason, or evidence of some non-compliance, before a Building Control Authority institutes proceedings. Since requirements in the Regulations are usually broadly stated - "provide adequate ventilation", for example - demonstrating either compliance or non-compliance may not be easy. Expert opinion will be important in arriving at a final decision one way or the other.

Designers will want to be in a position to provide clients and others with documented evidence that they have properly designed, and adequately assessed, the project in terms of sustainability and compliance with the Regulations at the design stage. Maintaining a 'paper trail' of records which demonstrate that they have considered and met the requirements of any Regulations will be important. In these situations it would probably be reasonable for a designer to rely on official publications, or publications based on the outcome of research at a reputable institution. Material accepted in another EU Member State - French material on heat loss calculations, or Danish advice on the re-use of recycled materials, for example - would probably also be authoritative if it is appropriate for use in Irish conditions.

Until sustainable methods and strategies are integrated into mainstream Irish building design and practice, and into official Irish publications, the designer wishing to design in a sustainable manner will be more exposed than is the designer content with conventional practice. A discussion with the client on Statutory requirements, together with a review of how those requirements are being met, would be good practice and in the client's interest.

The design, construction and maintenance of buildings in Ireland is subject to many legal controls, and a comprehensive review of their potential impact on sustainable design is beyond the scope of this manual. The general implications of some statutory requirements which clearly have relevance for sustainable design are considered here. Comments on specific requirements in relation to ventilation, heat loss and other issues will be found in the appropriate Sections in Part B.

I   BUILDING REGULATIONS

The Building Control Act, 1990, does not in itself contain requirements for sustainable design, but under the Act Regulations may be made for energy conservation, the efficient use of resources, good building practice, and health, safety and welfare. All of these relate to sustainable design and construction practices, and the Regulations made under the Act and the Technical Guidance Documents which support them do, in fact, include many requirements which have implications for sustainability.

The clauses which have the most extensive impact are probably those in Part L, which requires that "a building shall be so designed and constructed as to secure, in so far as is reasonably practicable, the conservation of fuel and energy." The technical guidance to Part L is extensive and covers heat loss through the building fabric, controls for space heating and hot water systems, and the insulation of hot water storage vessels, pipes and ducts. However, the energy conservation measures proposed are relatively underdeveloped. There is no advice on choice of fuel, on energy conservation in relation to building ventilation, on limiting air conditioning, or on optimising total building energy consumption. The calculation methods and advice on passive measures to maximise solar gain during the heating season are limited.

The requirements of Part C in relation to contaminants and other substances found on or under the site are accompanied by guidance on site investigation and remedial measures. In relation to radon gas, the Nuclear Energy Board (since replaced by the Radiological Protection Institute of Ireland) is to be consulted for information on affected areas. Guidance on appropriate measures to be taken is contained in the Department of the Environment's publication *Radon in Buildings*.

Guidance to Part F, Ventilation, indicates that uncontrolled permanent ventilation to dwellings is desirable. This increases energy consumption for space heating. Part G, which covers hygiene, is silent on issues of water conservation at point of use. Part H covers drainage, and gives guidance on the adequate and hygienic disposal of foul and surface water. This allows reasonable freedom in the selection of waste treatment systems, but advice is limited to septic tank design and location. There is no indication of the existence of other, more sustainable, methods of waste treatment.

Finally, in relation to building materials, the use of products containing CFCs is discouraged.

The Department of the Environment is at present (February 1996) revising the Technical Guidance Documents to the Building Regulations. The extent of the proposed revisions varies from Part to Part, and in most cases changes are unrelated to sustainable building. However the Guidance Document for Part L is being extensively re-written. The need for an integrated approach to energy conservation at the design stage, and the possible use of energy/environmental audits or ratings, are noted. The Part F requirement for permanent ventilation is likely to be modified.

2   PLANNING REGULATIONS

The 1963-1994 Local Government (Planning and development) Acts and Regulations contain no specific requirements for sustainable architecture or sustainable building. Development Plans adopted by Planning Authorities are beginning to embody implicit and/or explicit aspirations towards sustainable settlement. The promotion of public over private transport, and the promotion of high quality, and therefore durable, design and construction are two examples. This may generate a climate favourable to sustainable development proposals.

It is not difficult to imagine that, in the future, Planning Authorities might require water metering or closed systems for waste water treatment (which would gradually see the disappearance of the septic tank), or might develop land use policies to promote sustainable locations for new settlements.

3   SAFETY, HEALTH AND WELFARE AT WORK REGULATIONS

The Safety, Health and Welfare at Work Act, 1989, imposes duties on employers, designers, and others in relation to places of work. Most are general in nature; requirements for safety statements, consultation at the workplace, safety representatives and emergency duties, for example. There are no specific requirements in relation to sustainable design strategies, but places of work must be so designed that they are, so far as is reasonably practicable, safe and without risk to health. Fresh air is required and natural light encouraged. There is no guidance on how these requirements may be met.

4   ENVIRONMENTAL IMPACT ASSESSMENT

The European Communities (Environmental Impact Assessment) Regulations, S.I. 349 of 1989, requires that, for certain kinds of development, an Environmental Impact Statement be submitted, usually to the Planning Authority. Developments subject to the regulations include: industrial estates over 15 hectares; large urban development projects; holiday villages with more than 100 holiday homes; waste water treatment plants; and many infrastructural, chemical, agricultural, mining, and marine projects. (The Directive which these Regulations transpose has recently been reviewed, but in general the criteria for developments falling within the regulations show little change.) The Statement must include an assessment of the likely impact on people, flora, fauna, soil, water, air, climate, landscape, material assets, cultural heritage, and a description of measures envisaged to reduce or avoid adverse effects.

The procedures are intended to reduce adverse environmental impact and ought to encourage sustainable development. They do not prescribe specific measures of sustainability to be undertaken, leaving this to the discretion of the persons making the proposals.

A design team which is pursuing sustainable strategies will, in any case, be assessing environmental impact throughout the design process, and should find itself in a strong position in relation to the regulations.

5   EC CONSTRUCTION PRODUCTS REGULATIONS

Under the European Communities (Construction Products) Regulations, S.I. 198 of 1992, construction products should not be placed on the market unless they enable the buildings into which they are to be incorporated to meet the "essential requirements" set out in Council Directive 89/106/EEC. Some of the essential requirements have implications for sustainability, although more by proscribing unsatisfactory materials than by promoting sustainable ones:

- buildings must not endanger hygiene or health by way of toxic gases, dangerous particles in the air, dangerous radiation, pollution or poisoning of water or soil, faulty elimination of waste water, smoke, solid or liquid wastes;
- buildings must be designed and built so as to keep noise perceived by occupants or neighbours to a level which will not threaten health and will allow them to sleep, rest and work;
- the works and their heating, cooling and ventilation installations must be designed and built so that the amount of energy required in use shall be low, having regard to the climatic conditions of the location and the occupants.

The regulations are enforced by the Building Control Authorities, and the requirements must be met in any building which is subject to Regulations which contain those requirements. However, the Irish Building Regulations omit some of the requirements. At present, therefore, building products used in Ireland are regulated in respect to some, but not all, issues covered by the EC (Construction Products) Regulations.

FURTHER READING

- Edwards, Brian. *Towards Sustainable Architecture: European Directives and Building Design.* Oxford, Butterworth Architecture, 1996.

- O'Cofaigh, E. *The Building Regulations Explained.* Dublin, Royal Institute of the Architects of Ireland, 1993. £30.

- Keane, David. *Building and the Law.* 2nd edition. Dublin, Royal Institute of the Architects of Ireland, 1993. The third edition, due to be published in 1996, will cover environmental law as it applies to buildings. £30.

- *RIAI Technical Information Microfile.* Microfiche service published jointly by the RIAI, RIBA Companies Ltd., and Technical Indexes Ltd. Contains full texts of a wide selection of Irish legislation covering all aspects of the design process. *Contact: RIAI, 8 Merrion Square, Dublin 2. Tel (01) 676 1703 Fax (01) 661 0948*

APPENDIX I

DECLARATION OF INTERDEPENDENCE FOR A SUSTAINABLE FUTURE
UIA / AIA World Congress of Architects, Chicago, 18 - 21 June 1993

In recognition that:

A sustainable society restores, preserves, and enhances nature and culture for the benefit of all life, present and future; • a diverse and healthy environment is intrinsically valuable and essential to a healthy society; • today's society is seriously degrading the environment and is not sustainable;

We are ecologically interdependent with the whole natural environment; • we are socially, culturally, and economically interdependent with all of humanity; sustainability, in the context of this interdependence, requires partnership, equity and balance among all parties;

Buildings and the built environment play a major role in the human impact on the natural environment and on the quality of life; • sustainable design integrates consideration of resource and energy efficiency, healthy buildings and materials, ecologically and socially sensitive land-use; and an aesthetic sensitivity that inspires, affirms and ennobles; • sustainable design can significantly reduce adverse human impacts on the natural environment while simultaneously improving quality of life and economic well-being;

We commit ourselves,

as members of the world's architectural and building-design professions, individually and through our professional organisations, to:

- Place environmental and social sustainability at the core of our practices and professional responsibilities
- Develop and continually improve practices, procedures, products, curricula, services, and standards that will enable the implementation of sustainable design
- Educate our fellow professionals, the building industry, clients, students, and the general public about the critical importance and substantial opportunities of sustainable design
- Establish policies, regulations, and practices in government and business that ensure sustainable design becomes normal practice
- Bring all existing and future elements of the built environment - in their design, production, use and eventual reuse - up to sustainable design standards.

Olufemi Majekodunmi
President
International Union of Architects

Susan A Maxman
President
American Institute of Architects

APPENDIX 2

CYLINDRICAL SUNPATH DIAGRAM

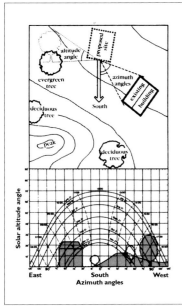

Plotting the skyline. Source: Achard & Gicquel, 1986

Although the facade of a building may have a favourable orientation, the sun may be obstructed for some or all of the day by other buildings, trees or land forms. The degree of obstruction depends on latitude, season and time of day, and on the disposition of obstructions. Obstruction can be assessed using (a) a Cylindrical Sunpath Diagram for the site's latitude, together with (b) a plan of the relevant building facade, in correct orientation and with surrounding obstructions. The heights of the obstructions should be noted on the plan.

Step 1. Draw lines from the reference point on the building facade to the points that define the main obstructions in plan. Note the horizontal (azimuth) angles relative to South (clockwise W, anti-clockwise E).

Step 2. For each line defining an obstruction on plan note the corresponding elevation angle. This can be found by drawing a section, but is probably easier to calculate using the equation

$$\tan^{-1} h / d$$

where   **h** is the height, and
        d is the distance from the reference point for each obstruction point.

Step 3. Each obstruction point is now defined by its horizontal and vertical angle. Mark these points on the Cylindrical Sunpath Diagram, and join the points logically. (Points on the same obstructing object are joined together.) Edges which are vertical in reality remain vertical on the diagram.

Step 4. Shade-in the areas representing obstructions on the diagram. Areas of the diagram which are not overlaid by shading represent periods during which the sun has access to the reference point.

By carrying out this procedure for a number of selected reference points it is possible to assess solar access to the proposed building or to the site as a whole.

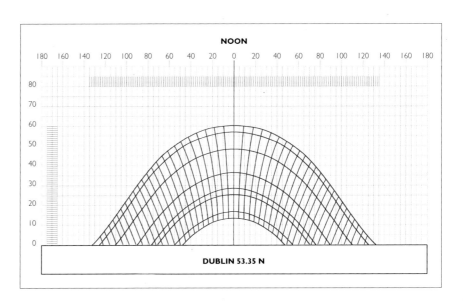

APPENDIX 3

DRAFT QUESTIONNAIRE For use in Product Enquiries.

Have you carried out any assessment of the ecological impact of the production, supply, use and recycling of your product?

Please give quantified details of your products under the following headings:

Natural Resources Used
Petroleum
Water
Wood
Minerals

Energy Used
Oil/Gas
Electricity

Solid Wastes
Production
Product
Packaging

Air Emissions
Carbon Dioxide
Sulphur Oxides
Nitrogen Oxides
Carbon Monoxide
Particulates

Water Emissions
COD
Metals
BOD
Suspended Solids
Organic Chemicals

What research programmes have you put in place to improve your materials in these respects?

If any, what time scale do you envisage?

What provision have you made for ease of recycling for your product / material?

APPENDIX 4

CALCULATING NET SOLAR GAIN

Step 1: Calculate Raw Solar Gain

The daily solar heat gain per month per unit of gross window aperture Q (kWh/m^2 day) may be calculated for each month using the following formula

$$Q = \sum (E \times A \times \tau \times m \times C_c \times S_f)$$

Where
- Q = solar gain (kWh/day)
- E = mean daily solar irradiation on plane of a given facade(kWh/m^2 day)*.
- A = window aperture area (including frames) for given facade (m^2).
- m = ratio of glazed area to aperture area.
- τ = transmittance of glazing. (Some typical values are given in Section B.5: Envelope)
- C_c = transmission factor for net curtains = 0.93 (typical value). If there are no curtains $C_c = 1$.
- S_f = shading factor. This accounts for the reduction in transmitted energy due to obstruction of solar energy by nearby buildings, trees, etc. If there are no obstructions $S_f = 1$.

* (Solar radiation data for Birr, Kilkenny and Valentia are given in the *European Solar Radiation Atlas, Volume II, Inclined Surfaces*. The tables include figures for vertical surfaces and surfaces at 10 °, 30 °, and 60° angles, for all orientations.)

Step 2: Calculate Window Heat Loss

Transmission losses Q_L (kWh/m^{2}day) for glazing can be calculated as follows:

$$Q_L = U \times \Delta T \times 24/1000$$

where
- U = U-value (W/m^{2}K) of the glazing and
- ΔT = difference between mean internal and external temperatures (K).

Mean monthly temperatures for various locations are given in Appendix 7. For other locations contact the Meteorological Service.

Step 3: Raw Solar Gain less Window Heat Loss = Net Solar Gain.

This calculation must be carried out for each orientation and for any variation in glazing type or degree of obstruction.

APPENDIX 5

CALCULATING SPACE HEATING REQUIREMENTS

A relatively simple method for estimating the space heating requirement of a building, taking account of direct solar gain, internal gains, and of transmission and ventilation heat losses, is described below. The method may be used for comparing alternative passive solar design proposals at the early design stage; computer simulations can provide more accurate estimates.

Other things being equal, the passive solar design proposal that produces the lowest annual space heating requirement is the most effective solution.

The procedure involves calculating, for each **month** of the heating season, the mean daily value of:

    (a) Heat Loss (transmission plus ventilation)
    (b) Heat Gain (solar plus internal)
    (c) Useful Heat Gain
    (d) Space Heating Requirement (to be met by active heating systems).

STEP I
CALCULATE MEAN DAILY HEAT LOSSES

Transmission (fabric) heat loss Q_t is given by the following equation:

$$Q_t = \Sigma\,(UA) \times (T_i - T_o) \times (24\,/\,1000)$$

where:

Q_t	=	transmission heat loss (kWh/day).
U	=	U-value of building element (W/m²K).
A	=	area of building element (m²).
$\Sigma\,(UA)$	=	sum of UA values for all elements of the building envelope (W/K).
T_i	=	mean monthly internal temperature (°C).
T_o	=	mean monthly external temperature (°C)*.
24 / 1000		converts from watts to kWh/day.

* (Mean monthly external temperatures for eight locations in Ireland are given in Appendix 7. For other locations consult the Meteorological Service.)

Ventilation heat loss Q_v is given by the equation:

$$Q_v = n \times V \times 0.34 \times (T_i - T_o) \times 24\,/\,1000$$

where:

Q_v	=	ventilation heat loss (kWh/day).
n	=	average number of air changes per hour (h⁻¹).
V	=	volume of heated space (m³).
0.34		converts from m³/h to W/K

(For ventilation systems with heat recovery, account should be taken of the reduction in ventilation heat loss.)

Total heat loss **Q**, in kWh/day, is then given by the equation:

$$Q = Q_t + Q_v$$

STEP 2
CALCULATE MEAN DAILY HEAT GAINS

Internal heat gain Q_i includes gains from people, processes, hot water, lighting, electrical equipment and machinery.

Q_i is calculated by estimating and then summing the total gains from each of these sources. (Some nominal values for internal gains are given in Section B.6, paragraph 1.5.)

Solar gain via the windows Q_s is given by the equation:

$$Q_s = (E \times A \times m \times \tau \times C_c \times S_f)$$

where:

Q_s	=	solar gain (kWh/day).
E	=	mean daily solar irradiation on plane of a given facade (kWh/m²day).*
A	=	window aperture area for facade (including frames) (m²)
m	=	ratio of glazed area to aperture area.**
τ	=	transmittance of glazing.***
C_c	=	transmission factor for net curtains. A typical value is 0.93. If there are no net curtains, $C_c = 1$.
S_f	=	shading factor.****

*   (Solar radiation data for Birr, Kilkenny and Valentia are given in the *European Solar Radiation Atlas, Volume II, Inclined Surfaces.* The tables include figures for vertical surfaces and surfaces at 10 °, 30 °, and 60° angles, for all orientations.)

**   (m is the proportion of window aperture area occupied by the glazing itself. If window-frames account for 15% of window aperture area, m = 0.85.)

***   (While transmittance varies with glazing type, typical values are 0.84 for single glazing, 0.72 for double glazing and 0.65 for low-e double glazing. The reduction in transmittance due to average levels of dust or dirt on windows should also be accounted for.)

****   (The shading factor takes account of the reduction in solar radiation due to adjacent buildings, trees, etc. For unshaded windows, Sf = 1.)

Q_s must be calculated for each orientation and the results summed to give solar gain for the entire building.

STEP 3
CALCULATE USEFUL HEAT GAIN

Not all of the internal and solar gains contribute to reducing the space heating requirement of the building. Some will result in overheating and/or the opening of windows, and some will be received at times when heating is not required. These effects are accounted for by means of a utilisation factor.

The value of this utilisation factor depends largely on the ratio of internal and solar gains (Q_i and Q_s) to the total heat loss (Q). This is known as the gain-loss ratio or GLR. It also depends on the building's thermal mass, the speed of response of the heating system, occupant behaviour, occupancy patterns, thermal zoning within the building, etc

The utilisation factor **UF** for each month may be estimated using the equation:

$$UF = (1 - GLR^a) / (1 - GLR^{a+1})$$

where **a** is a constant depending on the building in question. Typical values of **a** for buildings of low, medium and high utilisation factor are 0.8, 1.8 and 3.3 respectively. If in doubt, the medium value, a = 1.8, may be used. Utilisation factor curves are illustrated below.

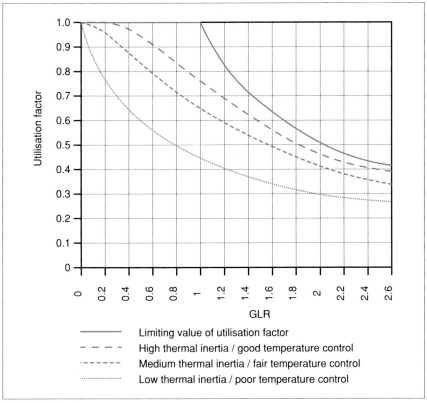

Utilisation factor curves

Useful solar and internal gain is then obtained by multiplying total gain by the utilisation factor:

Useful heat gain = UF x (Q$_s$ + Q$_i$)

STEP 4
CALCULATE DAILY SPACE HEATING REQUIREMENT

The **daily** space heating requirement is found by subtracting useful heat gain from total heat loss (Q).

STEP 5
CALCULATE MONTHLY SPACE HEATING REQUIREMENT

Multiply the daily values for each month by 30 to obtain **monthly** space heating requirements.

STEP 6
CALCULATE ANNUAL SPACE HEATING REQUIREMENT

The total annual space heating requirement is obtained by summing the monthly values for all months of the year for which a heating requirement is found to exist.

WORKED EXAMPLE

As an example, the annual space heating requirement of an imaginary building in Birr was estimated using this method. The building is described below, and the results are given in table 3 and the figure below.

The building is 20 m long, 8 m wide and 6 m high, with the long facades facing north/south. Windows occupy 30% of the south facade, and 20% of the north facade, with no glazing on the east and west facades. Window frames occupy 15% of window area, all windows have low-emittance double glazing, and all windows are unshaded. The mean U value of the building is 0.4 W/m²K. For all months, there are an average of 0.5 air changes per hour, internal gains amount to 60 kWh/day, and the mean internal temperature is 18°C. A "medium" utilisation factor (a = 1.8) applies.

Table 1: Mean monthly external temperatures at Birr, Co. Offaly.

Month	J	F	M	A	M	J	J	A	S	O	N	D
Mean temp.(°C)	4.4	4.6	6.3	8.1	10.7	13.4	14.8	14.7	13.0	10.4	6.5	5.4

Table 2: Estimated monthly means of daily global radiation on vertical planes at Birr, Co. Offaly (kWh/m²day).

Month	J	F	M	A	M	J	J	A	S	O	N	D
South	1.24	2.04	2.53	2.89	2.76	2.77	2.54	2.55	2.73	2.08	1.69	1.18
SE/SW	0.97	1.67	2.27	2.86	2.93	2.99	2.70	2.58	2.54	1.74	1.31	0.90
E/W	0.51	1.03	1.69	2.48	2.84	3.02	2.67	2.34	2.01	1.15	0.69	0.44
NE/NW	0.29	0.57	1.08	1.81	2.31	2.56	2.24	1.81	1.35	0.69	0.36	0.22
North	0.27	0.49	0.86	1.39	1.87	2.14	1.88	1.45	1.05	0.60	0.34	0.21

Table 3: Monthly space heating requirement of example building in Birr

Month	J	F	M	A	M	J	J	A	S	O	N	D
Heat loss (kWh/d)	139	137	120	101	75	47	33	34	51	78	117	129
Internal gain (kWh/d)	60	60	60	60	60	60	60	60	60	60	60	60
Solar gain (kWh/d)	28	47	62	76	80	83	75	70	68	49	38	26
Total gain (kWh/d)	88	107	122	136	140	143	135	130	128	109	98	86
Gain/loss ratio	0.6	0.8	1.0	1.3	1.9	3.1	4.1	3.9	2.5	1.4	0.8	0.7
Utilisation factor	0.78	0.72	0.64	0.55	0.44	0.30	0.23	0.24	0.35	0.53	0.70	0.76
Useful gain (kWh/d)	68	77	78	74	61	43	31	31	45	58	69	66
Space ht rqt (kWh/d)	70	60	42	27	14	4	2	2	6	20	49	63

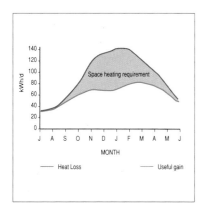

Space heating requirement of example building in Birr

APPENDIX 6

NORMALISED PERFORMANCE INDICATOR

The Normalised Performance Indicator (NPI) is obtained by applying 'normalising factors' to the energy consumed by an existing building over a given year. The NPI rating is based on limited information about the building.

The procedure, which assesses the potential for energy savings, can be used to judge whether an energy audit of the building is justified, or to rank a number of buildings in order of their energy, or money, saving possibilities.

STEP 1
CONVERT ENERGY UNITS TO kWh.

Obtain copies of all energy bills (electricity, gas, oil, etc.) for the past year. The table below shows the conversion factors to be used to convert from commonly used billing units to kilowatt hours (kWh).

Fuel type	Billing units	To get kWh multiply by:
Natural gas	Therms or cubic feet	29.31 or 0.303
Gas oil (35 sec)	Litres	10.6
Light fuel oil (290 sec)	Litres	11.2
Medium fuel oil (950 sec)	Litres	11.3
Heavy fuel oil (3500 sec)	Litres	11.4
Coal*	Tonnes	7600
Anthracite	Tonnes	9200
Liquid petroleum		
Gas (LPG)	Litres or tonnes	7 or 13900

*The calorific value of solid fuel will vary with its source. For a more accurate figure refer to supplier.

STEP 2
CALCULATE THE ENERGY USED FOR SPACE HEATING

This figure should include any electricity used for space heating. This can often be difficult to determine. Where a central plant provides both space heating and hot water then the latter must be subtracted from the total. If the space and water heating energy are not metered separately, the base energy load (energy used for hot water) can be established by plotting a bar chart of annual energy consumption. Alternatively, an approximate assessment of space heating can be obtained by assuming it to be 75% of the overall space and water heating energy consumption.

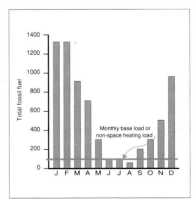

Notional bar chart of annual energy consumption. Consumption during the months when space heating is switched off gives an indication of the amount of energy used for hot water heating.

STEP 3
MODIFY SPACE HEATING ENERGY TO ACCOUNT FOR WEATHER

To take account of variations in consumption due to variations in weather conditions from year to year, a degree day correction factor is applied.

Degree day correction factor = $\dfrac{\text{Standard Degree Days (2462)}}{\text{Degree Days for Year Examined*}}$

* This information may be available from the Meteorological Service.
Since the difference between the two figures is often very small, the degree day correction factor may be close to '1'. If degree day figures for the location are not available then '1' can be used, although it will introduce an error.

Multiply the figure produced by Step 2 by the Degree Day Correction Factor.

STEP 4
MODIFY SPACE HEATING ENERGY TO ACCOUNT FOR EXPOSURE

Air infiltration due to building exposure can result in higher than normal levels of

Description of location	Factor
Sheltered: The building is in a built-up area with other buildings of similar height or greater surrounding it. Typical of city centre locations.	1.1
Normal: The building is on level ground in urban or rural surroundings. It would be usual to have trees and buildings adjacent.	1.0
Exposed: Coastal and hilly sites with little or no adjacent screening.	0.9

energy consumption. The following table gives correction factors for various locations.

Multiply the figure produced by Step 3 by the Exposure Correction Factor. You now have a normalised figure for energy consumption due to space heating.

STEP 5
ADD NON-HEATING ENERGY USE

Add all non-heating energy uses. These need not be normalised. Continue to use kilowatt hours.

STEP 6
MODIFY TOTAL ENERGY TO ALLOW FOR HOURS OF USE

Different buildings will have varying hours-of-use profiles. The most common profile for non-domestic buildings is from 09:00 to 17:00. However, other buildings, or parts of buildings may require continuous heating, cooling and/or ventilation. For the purposes of comparison this must be corrected.

From the table below select the building type that most closely describes your project and note the standard hours.

Type of building	Hours of use
Offices over 2000 m²	2600
Offices 2000 m² or less	2400
Offices or parts of offices occupied 24 hours per day	8760
Computer rooms	8760
Hospitals	8760
Universities (non-residential)	3500
Hotels	8760
Schools, Primary	1480
Schools, Secondary without indoor pool	1660

$$\text{Hours of Use Correction Factor} = \frac{\text{Standard number of hours}}{\text{Number of hours for your building}}$$

Allowance for additional hours of use:

If part of a building is used for a longer period than normal, an adjustment has to be made. This is best illustrated by an example.

Eighty percent of the floor area of an office building is normally open for 3120 hours per year; the remaining 20 percent is open for 8760 hours per year.

For 80% of the building the hours of use factor is:

$$\frac{2400}{3120} = 0.77$$

For the remaining 20% it is:

$$\frac{2400}{8760} = 0.27$$

For the whole building it is:

$$(0.8 \times 0.77) + (0.2 \times 0.27) = 0.67$$

If the Hours of Use Correction Factor is greater than 1.33 or less than 0.67 then the upper or lower limit should be used as no comparative data is available outside of this range.

Multiply the Total Energy Use obtained in Step 5 by the Hours of Use Correction Factor. You now have the Corrected Annual Energy Consumption for your building.

STEP 7
CALCULATE FLOOR AREA (m²)

STEP 8
CALCULATE THE NORMALISED PERFORMANCE INDICATOR (NPI)

$$NPI = \frac{Corrected\ Annual\ Energy\ Consumption}{Floor\ Area}$$

This Performance Indicator indicates the energy consumption for your building under standard conditions.

Comparing your Building with Other Buildings

Energy Efficiency Rating	Good	Fair	Poor
Type of building			
Offices (air conditioned)			
over 2000m²	<250	250-410	>410
2000m² or less	<220	220-310	>310
Offices (naturally ventilated)			
over 2000 m²	<230	230-290	>290
2000m² or less	<200	200-250	>250
Computer centres	<340	340-480	>480
Hospitals			
Small acute (< 25,000 m²)	<450	450-600	>600
Large acute (> 25,000 m²)	<525	525-600	>600
Universities	<325	325-355	>355
Hotels			
Large	<290	290-420	>420
Small hotels and guest houses	<240	240-330	>330
Schools			
Primary	<180	180-240	>240
Secondary (no indoor pool)	<190	190-240	>240
Sports buildings			
Swimming pool	<1050	1050-1390	>1390
Sports centre without swimming pool	<200	200-340	>340

This NPI procedure and the ratings which accompany it are based on material published by the Energy Efficiency Offices of the UK. Department of Energy and UK Department of the Environment, who publish a series of booklets on NPI procedures for a wider range of building types.

APPENDIX 7

CLIMATE DATA

The Meteorological Service maintains records returned by a large number of stations. All return daily values of temperature and rainfall while some also measure humidity, sunshine and wind. Eleven - Valentia Observatory, Phoenix Park in Dublin, Malin Head, Markree Castle, Roche's Point, Rosslare, Kilkenny, Belmullet, Clones, Claremorris and Birr - provide hourly values of temperature, humidity, rainfall, sunshine, wind, cloud and pressure. Solar radiation is recorded at seven stations: Valentia Observatory, Kilkenny, Birr, Dublin Airport, Belmullet, Clones and Malin Head.

Climate data for Birr, Cork, Dublin, Malin Head, Markree Castle (Co. Sligo), Rosslare, Shannon and Valentia are presented in this Appendix. These eight stations were selected on the basis that they demonstrate fairly well the range of climate conditions in Ireland and/or are located close to large centres of population.

The tables show mean monthly values for climate factors relevant to sustainable design. Where figures for a particular climate variable are not shown, it is because the information is not available.

For further information, or for climate data about other locations, contact the Irish Meteorological Service, Climate Enquiries, Glasnevin Hill, Dublin 9. Tel. (01) 842 4411, Fax (01) 836 9115.

Other Sources of Data

Work carried out within various European Commission programmes has produced additional information which can sometimes be helpful, particularly where simulation exercises are planned. The results are presented in the publications listed below.

- CEC European Wind Atlas. Troen, I and Peterson, E. L. Riso National Laboratory, P.O. Box 49, DK-4000 Roskilde, Denmark. 1989.

- Commission of the European Communities. European Solar Radiation Atlas, Vol. I. (2nd edition) Kasten, F., Golchert, H. J.., Dogniaux, R., Lemoine, M. and W. Palz, Eds. Verlag TUV Rheinland, Cologne. 1984.

- Commission of the European Communities. European Solar Radiation Atlas, Volume II, Inclined Surfaces. Page, J. K.., Flynn, R. J.., Dogniaux, R. and Preuveneers, G., Editor, W. Palz, Verlag, TUV, Rheinland. 1984.

- EUFRAT Climatic Data Handbook: Climatic Data for the Design of Renewable Energy Systems in Europe: frequency distribution of solar radiation and temperature. Bourges, B. Ed. CEC, Brussels. 1990.

- Short Reference Years and Test Reference Years for the EEC Countries. Technical University of Denmark, Thermal Insulation Laboratory, Final Report Contract ESF-029-DK, Lund, H. Report EUR 9402, published by the Thermal Insulation Laboratory, Building 118, Technical University of Denmark, DK-2800 Lyngby, Denmark. 1985.

- Test Reference Years TRYs: weather data sets for computer simulations of solar energy systems and energy consumption in buildings. Lund, H. Report No. EUR 9765, Commission of the European Communities, Brussels. 1985.

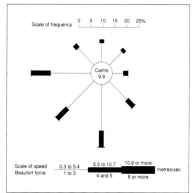

Wind rose diagram; Birr

CLIMATE DATA FOR BIRR

Air Temperature (°C) for period 1951-1980

	Jan	Feb	Mar	Apr	May	Jun	Jul	Aug	Sep	Oct	Nov	Dec
Max	7.4	7.7	9.8	12.3	15.1	17.8	18.8	18.8	16.8	13.8	9.7	8.3
Min	1.3	1.4	2.7	3.8	6.3	9.0	10.8	10.5	9.1	6.9	3.3	2.5
Mean	4.4	4.6	6.3	8.1	10.7	13.4	14.8	14.7	13.0	10.4	6.5	5.4

Ground Temperature (C) at a depth of 100 mm below bare soil for period 1958-1982

Max	6.0	6.7	8.9	11.3	15.3	19.2	19.6	20.0	16.1	12.6	8.6	7.1
Min	0.8	1.5	4.5	7.9	10.9	13.8	15.5	15.1	12.1	8.0	4.6	2.8
Mean	4.0	4.5	6.2	9.4	12.9	16.5	17.5	16.8	14.1	10.6	6.5	4.7

Ground Temperature (C) at a depth of 300 mm below grass for period 1958-1982

Max	6.9	6.7	8.5	10.4	13.6	16.7	18.4	18.1	15.8	13.1	10.0	7.6
Min	1.1	1.7	4.9	7.9	10.4	13.4	15.1	15.2	13.3	9.7	6.5	4.3
Mean	4.8	5.1	6.5	9.0	12.0	15.1	16.4	16.3	14.5	11.5	8.0	5.9

Global (G) and Diffuse (D) Solar Radiation (J/cm²) for period 1977-1984

G	258	469	847	1338	1667	1719	1595	1353	1007	598	312	193
D	170	287	524	776	1004	1092	1048	891	619	353	191	131

Relative Humidity (%) for the hours 0600 and 1200 GMT

0600	90	90	90	91	90	91	92	93	92	91	90	90
1200	85	81	74	69	67	68	71	71	74	79	83	86

Sunshine (monthly averages of daily mean value of bright sunshine duration) for period 1951-1980

Mean	1.77	2.57	3.46	4.89	5.78	5.41	4.35	4.57	3.69	2.80	2.05	1.42
(%)	22	27	30	36	37	33	27	31	29	27	24	19

Wind (Mean monthly speed in m/sec and highest gust) for period 1962-1990

Mean speed	4.2	4.0	4.1	3.7	3.6	3.3	3.1	3.0	3.6	3.8	3.9	4.2
Max Gust	43.8	35.0	31.9	30.9	28.8	26.3	22.7	29.9	41.7	33.5	34.0	35.5

Rainfall (monthly averages of rainfall in mm and mean number of days with 1.0 mm or more) for period 1951-1980

Mean	76	52	53	55	62	52	68	76	79	80	77	86
Days	14	11	13	11	13	11	10	13	13	14	13	14

Degree Days below 15.5C for period 1958-1984

Mean	343	300	289	224	159	86	57	61	94	164	269	325

CLIMATE DATA FOR CORK

Air Temperature (°C) for period 1951-1980

	Jan	Feb	Mar	Apr	May	Jun	Jul	Aug	Sep	Oct	Nov	Dec
Max	8.5	9.0	10.9	13.3	16.2	18.8	19.9	20.1	17.7	14.3	10.9	9.2
Min	2.4	2.6	4.0	5.3	7.4	10.3	12.0	11.8	10.1	7.2	4.4	3.3
Mean	5.5	5.8	7.5	9.3	11.8	14.6	16.0	16.0	13.9	10.8	7.7	6.3

Ground Temperature (C) at a depth of 100 mm below bare soil for period 1958-1982

Max	7.3	7.8	9.2	11.4	15.2	18.1	18.4	18.5	16.7	13.7	10.3	8.3
Min	2.2	3.5	5.6	8.4	11.1	13.4	15.0	15.5	12.7	9.4	6.7	4.9
Mean	5.8	6.1	7.3	9.8	12.7	15.7	17.1	16.6	14.7	11.7	8.4	6.6

Ground Temperature (C) at a depth of 300 mm below grass for period 1958-1982

Max	8.1	8.1	8.7	10.5	13.8	16.2	16.4	16.3	15.5	13.8	11.3	8.9
Min	3.1	3.9	5.5	7.8	10.1	11.8	13.8	14.5	13.2	10.3	7.7	6.2
Mean	6.5	6.4	7.2	8.9	11.3	13.8	15.3	15.5	14.4	12.2	9.4	7.6

Relative Humidity (%) for the hours 0600 and 1200 GMT

0600	87	87	88	88	89	90	91	92	91	90	87	87
1200	84	82	79	75	76	78	78	78	80	81	82	84

Sunshine (monthly averages of daily mean value of bright sunshine duration) for period 1951-1980

Mean	2.00	2.65	3.54	5.42	6.42	6.38	5.62	5.33	4.25	3.04	2.34	1.76
(%)	25	27	30	40	42	39	35	37	34	29	27	23

Wind (Mean monthly speed in m/sec and highest gust) for period 1962-1990

Mean speed	6.4	6.2	6.1	5.5	5.3	4.7	4.4	4.5	5.1	5.7	5.8	6.3
Max Gust	48.4	33.5	36.1	32.4	30.9	26.3	23.7	25.8	33.0	38.6	34.0	35.0

Rainfall (monthly averages of rainfall in mm and mean number of days with 1.0mm or more) for period 1951-1980

Mean	148	106	103	70	87	64	73	90	115	120	115	139
Days	14	12	11	9	12	9	8	10	11	12	13	13

Degree Days below 15.5C for period 1958-1984

Mean	323	296	291	228	170	91	56	57	90	159	251	303

Air Pollution (mean winter concentrations of SO$_2$ and smoke)

SO$_2$ (in gr/m³)

Cork City	1989	1990	1991
Prince's St	21	11	13
St. Finbarr's Cemetery	22	20	25

Smoke (in gr/m³)

Cork City	1989	1990	1991
Prince's St	43	24	28
St. Finbarr's Cemetery	27	20	22

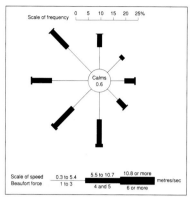

Wind rose diagram; Cork

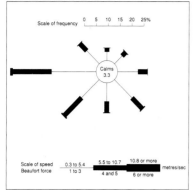

Wind rose diagram; Dublin

CLIMATE DATA FOR DUBLIN

Air Temperature (°C) for period 1951-1980

	Jan	Feb	Mar	Apr	May	Jun	Jul	Aug	Sep	Oct	Nov	Dec
Max	7.4	7.8	10.0	12.3	15.2	18.1	19.3	19.1	17.1	14.1	9.9	8.3
Min	1.5	1.4	2.5	3.6	6.0	8.9	10.8	10.5	8.9	6.8	3.6	2.5
Mean	4.5	4.6	6.3	8.0	10.6	13.5	15.1	14.8	13.0	10.5	6.8	5.4

Ground Temperature (C) at a depth of 100 mm below bare soil for period 1958-1982

	Jan	Feb	Mar	Apr	May	Jun	Jul	Aug	Sep	Oct	Nov	Dec
Max	5.8	6.4	8.5	10.7	14.6	18.5	19.4	19.6	16.0	12.9	9.0	6.8
Min	0.7	1.5	4.0	7.6	10.4	13.6	15.9	15.1	12.1	8.0	5.2	3.1
Mean	4.0	4.4	6.1	9.3	12.8	16.5	17.6	16.9	14.2	10.7	6.7	4.7

Ground Temperature (C) at a depth of 300 mm below grass for period 1958-1982

	Jan	Feb	Mar	Apr	May	Jun	Jul	Aug	Sep	Oct	Nov	Dec
Max	6.7	6.3	8.1	10.0	13.4	16.9	18.4	18.0	15.8	13.2	10.5	7.4
Min	1.8	2.1	4.2	7.2	9.9	12.9	15.0	14.7	12.9	9.3	6.2	4.7
Mean	4.7	4.9	6.1	8.7	11.9	15.3	16.5	16.3	14.4	11.4	7.9	5.7

Global (G) and Diffuse (D) Solar Radiation (J/cm^2) for period 1977-1984

	Jan	Feb	Mar	Apr	May	Jun	Jul	Aug	Sep	Oct	Nov	Dec
G	238	383	766	1290	1626	1678	1624	1365	903	557	284	166
D	142	243	462	710	900	1017	995	805	552	319	172	104

Relative Humidity (%) at 0600 and 1200 GMT

	Jan	Feb	Mar	Apr	May	Jun	Jul	Aug	Sep	Oct	Nov	Dec
0600	87	86	87	88	88	88	90	91	90	89	87	87
1200	82	79	73	69	70	69	71	72	73	77	80	82

Sunshine (monthly averages of daily mean value of bright sunshine duration) for period 1951-1980

	Jan	Feb	Mar	Apr	May	Jun	Jul	Aug	Sep	Oct	Nov	Dec
Mean	1.88	2.66	3.57	5.43	6.29	6.41	5.27	5.22	4.27	3.21	2.29	1.69
(%)	24	28	31	39	40	38	32	36	34	31	27	23

Wind (Mean monthly speed in m/sec and highest gust) for period 1962-1990

	Jan	Feb	Mar	Apr	May	Jun	Jul	Aug	Sep	Oct	Nov	Dec
Mean speed	6.3	5.8	5.9	5.1	4.5	4.3	4.1	4.0	4.6	5.1	5.7	6.1
Max Gust	38.6	37.6	29.9	31.9	28.8	28.8	27.8	28.8	33.0	37.6	34.5	36.6

Rainfall (monthly averages of rainfall in mm and mean number of days with 1.0 mm or more) for period 1951-1980

	Jan	Feb	Mar	Apr	May	Jun	Jul	Aug	Sep	Oct	Nov	Dec
Mean	68	51	50	47	58	53	59	75	73	68	69	79
Days	12	10	11	10	12	10	9	11	11	11	11	12

Degree Days below 15.5C for period 1958-1984

	Jan	Feb	Mar	Apr	May	Jun	Jul	Aug	Sep	Oct	Nov	Dec
Mean	330	295	288	224	156	78	51	52	81	152	254	311

Air Pollution (mean winter concentrations of SO$_2$ and smoke)

SO$_2$ (in gr/m^3)

Dublin City	1989	1990	1991
Ballsbridge	43	22	27
Clontarf	27	28	31
Clondalkin	32	32	34

Smoke (in gr/m^3)

Dublin City	1989	1990	1991
Ballsbridge	32	20	25
Clontarf	25	15	18
Clondalkin	27	25	26

CLIMATE DATA FOR MALIN HEAD

Air Temperature (°C) for period 1951-1980

	Jan	Feb	Mar	Apr	May	Jun	Jul	Aug	Sep	Oct	Nov	Dec
Max	7.5	7.4	8.8	10.4	12.8	15.2	16.2	16.6	15.3	13.1	9.9	8.6
Min	3.0	2.8	3.8	5.2	7.4	9.8	11.4	11.6	10.5	8.7	5.4	4.2
Mean	5.3	5.1	6.3	7.8	10.1	12.5	13.8	14.1	12.9	10.9	7.7	6.4

Relative Humidity (%) for the hours 0600 and 1200 GMT

	Jan	Feb	Mar	Apr	May	Jun	Jul	Aug	Sep	Oct	Nov	Dec
0600	84	83	83	84	84	86	88	88	86	85	82	84
1200	81	79	76	76	76	78	81	80	78	79	80	81

Sunshine (monthly averages of daily mean value of bright sunshine duration) for period 1951-1980

	Jan	Feb	Mar	Apr	May	Jun	Jul	Aug	Sep	Oct	Nov	Dec
Mean	1.32	2.27	3.42	5.28	6.45	6.05	4.39	4.68	3.68	2.42	1.55	0.93
(%)	18	24	29	38	40	35	26	32	29	23	19	13

Wind (Mean monthly speed in m/sec and highest gust) for period 1962-1990

	Jan	Feb	Mar	Apr	May	Jun	Jul	Aug	Sep	Oct	Nov	Dec
Mean speed	9.6	9.1	8.8	7.6	7.0	6.6	6.5	6.4	7.9	8.9	9.5	9.8
Max Gust	46.9	47.9	46.4	37.1	36.6	38.1	27.8	34.5	50.5	41.7	39.1	45.3

Rainfall (monthly averages of rainfall in mm and mean number of days with 1.0 mm or more) for period 1951-1980

	Jan	Feb	Mar	Apr	May	Jun	Jul	Aug	Sep	Oct	Nov	Dec
Mean	106	75	71	57	58	71	80	88	101	105	119	112
Days	18	13	15	12	13	13	12	14	16	18	20	19

Degree Days below 15.5C

	Jan	Feb	Mar	Apr	May	Jun	Jul	Aug	Sep	Oct	Nov	Dec
Mean	311	288	285	228	169	91	62	58	84	140	241	286

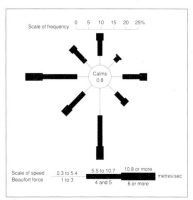

Wind rose diagram; Malin Head

CLIMATE DATA FOR MARKREE CASTLE

Air Temperature (°C) for period 1951-1980

	Jan	Feb	Mar	Apr	May	Jun	Jul	Aug	Sep	Oct	Nov	Dec
Max	7.2	7.8	9.9	12.3	15.1	17.5	18.3	18.5	16.6	13.8	9.8	8.3
Min	0.5	0.7	2.0	3.3	5.7	8.3	10.3	9.7	8.2	6.3	2.7	1.8
Mean	3.9	4.3	6.0	7.8	10.4	12.9	14.3	14.1	12.4	10.1	6.3	5.1

Relative Humidity (%) for the hours 0600 and 1200 GMT

	Jan	Feb	Mar	Apr	May	Jun	Jul	Aug	Sep	Oct	Nov	Dec
0600	86	86	85	87	87	87	90	91	89	87	85	85
1200	83	80	77	74	74	76	80	79	79	80	81	83

Sunshine (monthly averages of daily mean value of bright sunshine duration) for period 1951-1980

	Jan	Feb	Mar	Apr	May	Jun	Jul	Aug	Sep	Oct	Nov	Dec
Mean	1.56	2.58	3.64	5.46	6.48	5.97	4.50	5.03	3.85	2.74	1.73	1.09
(%)	20	27	31	40	41	35	27	34	31	26	21	15

Wind (Mean monthly speed in m/sec and highest gust) for period 1962-1990

	Jan	Feb	Mar	Apr	May	Jun	Jul	Aug	Sep	Oct	Nov	Dec
Mean speed	7.6	6.9	7.1	6.3	6.4	6.2	6.0	5.6	6.7	7.5	7.2	7.4
Max Gust	48.4	46.9	45.3	34.5	35.5	37.6	27.3	31.4	43.3	43.8	39.1	45.8

Rainfall (monthly averages of rainfall in mm and mean number of days with 1.0 mm or more) for period 1951-1980

	Jan	Feb	Mar	Apr	May	Jun	Jul	Aug	Sep	Oct	Nov	Dec
Mean	115	77	77	65	74	80	87	96	108	113	122	125
Days	20	15	17	14	16	14	15	16	18	20	20	21

Degree Days below 15.5C for period 1958-1984

	Jan	Feb	Mar	Apr	May	Jun	Jul	Aug	Sep	Oct	Nov	Dec
Mean	349	310	305	242	174	106	66	72	108	182	272	325

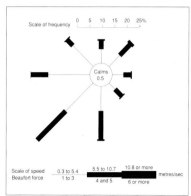

Wind rose diagram; Rosslare

CLIMATE DATA FOR ROSSLARE

Air Temperature (°C) for period 1951-1980

	Jan	Feb	Mar	Apr	May	Jun	Jul	Aug	Sep	Oct	Nov	Dec
Max	8.5	8.7	10.4	12.7	15.2	18.0	19.5	19.3	17.2	14.4	10.9	9.5
Min	2.3	2.5	3.7	4.8	7.1	9.7	11.6	11.3	9.8	7.8	4.3	3.4
Mean	5.4	5.6	7.1	8.8	11.2	13.9	15.6	15.3	13.5	11.1	7.6	6.5

Sunshine (monthly averages of daily mean value of bright sunshine duration) for period 1951-1980

	Jan	Feb	Mar	Apr	May	Jun	Jul	Aug	Sep	Oct	Nov	Dec
Mean	2.04	2.74	3.94	5.95	7.05	7.08	6.26	5.91	4.81	3.51	2.49	1.84
(%)	25	28	34	43	46	43	39	41	38	33	29	24

Wind (Mean monthly speed in m/sec and highest gust) for period 1962-1990

	Jan	Feb	Mar	Apr	May	Jun	Jul	Aug	Sep	Oct	Nov	Dec
Mean speed	6.7	6.6	6.5	6.1	5.9	5.3	4.8	5.0	5.5	6.0	6.3	6.6
Max Gust	39.1	38.1	31.9	38.6	29.4	26.3	29.9	28.8	37.1	44.8	38.1	41.2

Rainfall (monthly averages of rainfall in mm and mean number of days with 1.0 mm or more) for period 1951-1980

	Jan	Feb	Mar	Apr	May	Jun	Jul	Aug	Sep	Oct	Nov	Dec
Mean	95	69	63	54	59	49	59	73	79	90	99	98
Days	14	11	11	10	11	8	8	9	11	12	13	13

Degree Days below 15.5C

	Jan	Feb	Mar	Apr	May	Jun	Jul	Aug	Sep	Oct	Nov	Dec
Mean	293	267	268	208	149	74	41	37	63	121	221	271

Wind rose diagram; Shannon Airport

CLIMATE DATA FOR SHANNON AIRPORT

Air Temperature (°C) for period 1951-1980

	Jan	Feb	Mar	Apr	May	Jun	Jul	Aug	Sep	Oct	Nov	Dec
Max	8.9	9.1	10.2	12.0	13.8	16.1	17.2	17.8	16.5	14.3	11.0	9.7
Min	3.4	3.5	4.5	5.6	7.4	10.0	11.9	11.7	10.6	8.5	5.7	4.5
Mean	6.2	6.4	7.3	8.8	11.0	13.1	14.6	14.9	13.2	11.1	8.3	7.4

Relative Humidity (%) for the hours 0600 and 1200 GMT

	Jan	Feb	Mar	Apr	May	Jun	Jul	Aug	Sep	Oct	Nov	Dec
0600	87	87	88	88	89	90	91	92	91	90	87	87
1200	84	82	79	75	76	78	78	78	80	81	82	84

Sunshine (monthly averages of daily mean value of bright sunshine duration) for period 1951-1980

	Jan	Feb	Mar	Apr	May	Jun	Jul	Aug	Sep	Oct	Nov	Dec
Mean	1.70	2.62	3.48	5.05	6.00	5.01	4.63	4.69	3.74	2.75	1.94	1.45
(%)	21	27	30	37	39	34	29	32	30	26	23	19

Wind (Mean monthly speed in m/sec and highest gust) for period 1962-1990

	Jan	Feb	Mar	Apr	May	Jun	Jul	Aug	Sep	Oct	Nov	Dec
Mean speed	5.8	5.7	5.8	5.1	5.1	4.7	4.5	4.3	4.9	5.3	5.2	5.6
Max Gust	42.2	38.1	36.1	45.8	31.4	30.9	28.8	31.4	47.9	43.3	36.1	41.7

Rainfall (monthly averages of rainfall in mm and mean number of days with 1.0 mm or more) for period 1951-1980

	Jan	Feb	Mar	Apr	May	Jun	Jul	Aug	Sep	Oct	Nov	Dec
Mean	119	76	83	57	67	70	72	88	106	113	127	123
Days	16	12	13	11	13	11	11	13	14	15	16	16

Degree Days below 15.5C for period 1958-1984

	Jan	Feb	Mar	Apr	May	Jun	Jul	Aug	Sep	Oct	Nov	Dec
Mean	319	279	263	198	136	68	40	42	70	139	240	296

CLIMATE DATA FOR VALENTIA

Air Temperature (°C) for period 1951-1980

	Jan	Feb	Mar	Apr	May	Jun	Jul	Aug	Sep	Oct	Nov	Dec
Max	9.2	9.3	10.7	12.4	14.5	16.6	17.7	18.0	16.7	14.5	11.4	10.1
Min	3.9	3.6	4.8	5.9	7.9	10.3	11.9	12.0	10.8	9.0	6.2	5.2
Mean	6.6	6.5	7.8	9.2	11.2	13.5	14.8	15.0	13.8	11.8	8.8	7.7

Ground Temperature (°C) at a depth of 100 mm below bare soil for period 1958-1982

	Jan	Feb	Mar	Apr	May	Jun	Jul	Aug	Sep	Oct	Nov	Dec
Max	7.7	8.3	9.9	11.7	15.0	18.2	18.7	19.1	16.4	13.6	10.7	8.8
Min	1.1	3.1	6.1	8.9	11.4	13.4	15.9	15.1	12.5	9.4	6.8	4.7
Mean	5.9	6.3	7.7	10.2	13.1	16.1	17.2	16.7	14.6	11.7	8.4	6.7

Ground Temperature (°C) at a depth of 300 mm below grass for period 1958-1982

	Jan	Feb	Mar	Apr	May	Jun	Jul	Aug	Sep	Oct	Nov	Dec
Max	8.6	8.4	9.4	11.4	13.4	16.7	18.0	18.0	16.5	14.2	11.9	9.4
Min	2.5	3.4	5.9	8.7	10.8	13.5	15.5	14.6	13.1	10.6	7.7	5.8
Mean	6.8	6.8	8.0	10.0	12.5	15.1	16.4	16.3	14.9	12.3	9.5	7.8

Global (G) and Diffuse (D) Solar Radiation (J/cm²) for period 1977-1984

	Jan	Feb	Mar	Apr	May	Jun	Jul	Aug	Sep	Oct	Nov	Dec
G	260	514	901	1458	1845	1890	1746	1498	1035	605	312	196
D	161	255	491	729	961	1077	1006	862	563	334	178	124

Sunshine (monthly averages of daily mean value of bright sunshine duration) for period 1951-1980

	Jan	Feb	Mar	Apr	May	Jun	Jul	Aug	Sep	Oct	Nov	Dec
Mean	2.00	2.65	3.54	5.42	6.42	6.38	5.62	5.33	4.25	3.04	2.34	1.76
(%)	25	27	30	40	42	39	35	37	34	29	27	23

Wind (Mean monthly speed in m/sec and highest gust) for period 1962-1990

	Jan	Feb	Mar	Apr	May	Jun	Jul	Aug	Sep	Oct	Nov	Dec
Mean speed	6.8	6.3	6.1	5.3	5.4	4.7	4.3	4.5	5.3	5.9	6.2	6.5
Max Gust	44.8	43.3	34.0	37.6	34.5	31.9	26.8	36.1	45.3	38.1	43.8	43.3

Rainfall (monthly averages of rainfall in mm and mean number of days with 1.0 mm or more) for period 1951-1980

	Jan	Feb	Mar	Apr	May	Jun	Jul	Aug	Sep	Oct	Nov	Dec
Mean	162	118	115	79	85	76	86	98	128	142	151	159
Days	19	15	16	12	14	12	12	14	16	18	20	19

Degree Days below 15.5C for period 1958-1984

	Jan	Feb	Mar	Apr	May	Jun	Jul	Aug	Sep	Oct	Nov	Dec
Mean	275	249	244	193	142	76	47	43	68	125	203	254

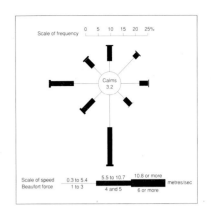

GLOSSARY

Active solar system
A system in which mechanical equipment is used to collect, store and distribute solar energy within the building.

Bentonite clay
A category of absorbent clay, used generally as filler.

Biofuel
Any fuel (solid, liquid or gas) produced from organic material from a sustainable source.

Biogas
Gas produced by decomposing organic material, including animal wastes and biomass.

Biomass
Organic materials produced by photosynthesis. Also, use of organic materials from sustainable sources (crops, human, animal or commercial wastes, for example) to generate heat or energy.

Combined heat and power(CHP)
The simultaneous use of one source to generate both electricity and thermal energy. Sometimes called 'cogeneration'.

Daylight factor
Illuminance at a specified point indoors, expressed as a percentage of the simultaneous horizontal illuminance outdoors under an unobstructed sky (percentage).

Degree Days
The product of the number of degrees below a given base temperature (15.5°C is the figure used in Ireland) and the number of days when that difference occurs. The heating degree day value for a year is calculated by taking the sum of the differences between the base temperature and the mean daily temperature for each day of the heating season. The base temperature of 15.5°C assumes a design temperature of 18°C, with a 2.4°C allowance for time lag and heat stored in the fabric of a building.

Direct radiation
Solar radiation coming directly from the sun.

Diffuse radiation
Solar radiation which is scattered in transmission through the atmosphere.

Embodied energy
The total amount of energy used in bringing the product or material to its present state and location (including harvesting/mining, processing, manufacture, and transport).

Grey water
Waste water discharged from sinks, basins, baths and washing machines.

Groundwater
Water found within the earth, in soil or in the crevices or pores of rock, which feeds springs and wells.

Heat pump
A thermodynamic device that transfers heat from one medium to another. The first medium (the source) cools, while the second (the heat sink) warms up.

Heat Exchanger
A mechanism whereby heat is transferred from a medium flowing on one side of a barrier to a medium flowing on the other. Often used to reclaim heat from outgoing ventilation air or waste water.

Heat recovery
Reclaiming heat which would otherwise be wasted. (see Heat Exchanger)

Hybrid system
A predominantly passive solar system in which some external power is used to move naturally heated or cooled air or water around the building.

Illuminance
The light striking unit area of a specified surface (lux)

Infiltration
Unwanted leakage of outdoor air into a building through cracks, joints, around door and window openings, etc.

Internal/Casual gains
Heat gains within a building resulting from occupants, lighting, and equipment (domestic appliances, office equipment, process machinery).

Life cycle analysis
Assessment of the total environmental impacts associated with a product's manufacture, use and disposal.

Luminance
Light emitted by unit area of matt surface, or, more generally, the intensity of light per unit area of surface seen from a given direction. It is expressed in candelas/m^2

Luminous efficacy
The ratio of the light emitted by a lamp to the energy consumed by it. It is expressed in lumens/W.

Macroclimate
The climate of a region.

Mass wall
A solid south-facing wall which absorbs solar radiation and transmits some of its heat into the building by conduction. The outer surface is generally given a matt black surface to increase absorption of solar radiation, and glazed to reduce heat loss to the outdoors.

Microclimate	The climate of a specific site or of a small area resulting from local topography.
Out-gassing/ Off-gassing	Emission of gases or volatile organic compounds from a material (solvents from paints, for example).
Passive solar systems	Systems which use the building elements to collect, store and distribute solar energy within the building.
Permaculture	A self-supporting system of agriculture, in which the organisation of plants and animals (including human animals) enables the continued recycling of nutrients and energy within the system, sustained ultimately by the input of solar energy.
Possible sunshine	Amount of time between sunrise and sunset when the sun is shining (expressed as a percentage).
Photovoltaic (PV) energy	Use of solar cells to generate electricity from solar radiation.
Primary energy	Energy value of a fuel at source. For oil this includes the energy costs of extraction and processing. For electricity it includes heat wasted in generation and distribution losses. In an oil or coal fired power station 33% of primary energy emerges in the form of electricity. The other 66% is waste heat vented to the atmosphere. So one unit of energy saved in a building represents 3 units of energy saved at the power plant.
Reflectance	Ratio or percentage of the quantity of light reflected by a surface to the amount of light striking that surface.
Shading coefficient	A measure of a window's ability to transmit solar heat gain, relative to the transmittance of a single sheet of 3 mm clear glass. Expressed as a value between 0 and 1, the lower the shading coefficient, the less heat the window transmits.
Sinks (out-gassing)	Materials which first absorb, and then release over an extended period, gases or compounds released by other materials.
Smart windows	Windows which respond to changes in thermal or lighting conditions. Windows with electrochromic, or photochromic glazing are two examples.
Super windows	Double or triple-glazed windows, gas filled and with low-e coating.
Sustainability	Managing the use of natural resources so that they are not irretrievably damaged or depleted.
Sustainable architecture	Architecture designed to limit, as far as is possible, depletion of or damage to the earth's natural resources or its human or animal populations.
Thermo-circulation	Natural circulation of air induced by increases and decreases in its density as it heats or cools.
Transmittance	Ratio of the radiant energy transmitted through a substance (e.g. glass) to the total radiant energy incident on its surface.
Trombe wall	Similar to a Mass Wall, but with vents at top and bottom. Air between wall and glazing is heated by the wall and rises, entering the living space through the upper vent, and drawing cool air from the living space through the bottom vent. Some heat is transmitted into the living space by conduction.
Turbidity	Lack of clarity or purity, usually with reference to air or water quality. Air turbidity is generally due to smoke, haze or and/dust
Utilisation factor (solar gain)	The percentage of incoming solar energy which actually displaces conventional or fossil fuelled heating.
Visible transmittance	A measure of the light in the visible portion of the spectrum which passes through glass. It is expressed by a number between 0 and 1.
Volatile organic compounds	Organic air pollutants resulting from evaporation or incomplete combustion.
Water wall	Similar in action to a Mass Wall, but constructed of water-filled metal, glass or plastic tubes or drums. Convection currents set up in the water transfer heat more rapidly through the wall.

REFERENCES

Achard, P. & R. Gicquel, editors. *European Passive Solar Hanbook: Basic Principles and concepts for passive solar architecture.* Preliminary edition. European Commission, 1986.

Baker, N., A. Fanchiotti and K. Steemers, Eds. *Daylighting in Architecture: A European Reference Book.* London, James & James for the European Commission, 1993

Baker, N. V. *Energy and Environment in Non-Domestic Buildings: a Technical Design Guide.* Cambridge, Cambridge Architectural Research Ltd., 1995.

Balaras, C. A., E. Daskalaki, M. Santamouris and A. Gaglia. *Indoor Comfort and Environmental Quality* . (Module 1: Design Principles). Published under a TEMPUS Joint European Project: Building Science and Environment-Conscious Design. London, Architectural Association School of Architecture for the European Commission, 1993.

Banham, Reyner. *The Architecture of the Well-Tempered Environment.* London, Architectural Press, 1969.

Barnett, Dianna Lopez and William D. Browning. *A Primer on Sustainable Building.* Snomass, Colo., Rocky Mountain Institute, 1995

Barton, Hugh, Geoff Davis and Richard Guise. *Sustainable settlements: a guide for planners, designers and developers.* Severnside Research and Consultancy Unit, Faculty of the Built Environment, University of the West of England. Luton, The Local Government Management Board, 1995.

Browning, William D. and Joseph Romm. *Greening the Building and the Bottom Line* Snomass, Colorado, Rocky Mountain Institute, 1994.

Burton, T. D. "The environmental equation: the impact of green issues." Paper delivered at 1st European Congress on Construction Economics, Paris, May 1993.

CEC European Wind Atlas. Troen, I and Peterson, E. L.. Risø National Laboratory, P.O. Box 49, DK-4000 Roskilde, Denmark. 1989

CIBSE Applications Manual: Window Design. London, Chartered Institution of Building Services Engineers (CIBSE), 1987.

Client's Guide to Greener Construction.(SP 120). Construction Industry Research and Information Association (CIRIA). London, CIRIA, 1995.

Crowther, D. R. G. and N. V.. Baker. 'Breathing walls: fact or fiction.' in *Solar Energy in Architecture and Urban Planning: 3rd European Conference on Architecture, Florence, May 1993.* Brussels, European Commission, 1993.

Davidson, Paul. *Energy Conservation in Retrofit.* Garston, Building Research Establishment, 1994.

Daylight : International Recommendations for the Calculation of Natural Daylight. (CIE Publication No. 16) Paris, Commission Internationale de l'Eclairage, 1970.

Denmark. National Building Agency. *Denmark Uses Energy Better.* 2nd. ed. Copenhagen, National Building Agency, 1987.

Department of the Environment. *Moving Towards Sustainability: a Review of Recent Environmental Policy and Developments.* Dublin, Department of the Environment, May 1995.

Energy Efficiency in Hotels: Good Energy Management in a Medium-Sized Hotel. (Good Practice Case Study 242). London, Energy Efficiency Office, 1995.

Energy Related Environmental Issues in Building: Sheet 14. Pack describing the EnREI Programme managed by the Building Research Establishment for the Construction Sponsorship Directorate of the Department of the Environment. Garston, BRE, [n.d.]

Environmental Protection Agency. *Advice Notes on Current Practice in the Preparation of Environmental Impact Statements.* Ardcavan, EPA, 1995.

EOLAS. *Pollution from Domestic Fuels.* (Energy and Environment Information Sheet No.5). Dublin, EOLAS [n.d.]

European Solar Radiation Atlas, Volume II, Inclined Surfaces. Page, J. K.., Flynn, R. J., Dogniaux, R. and Preuveneers, G. Editor, W. Palz, Verlag TUV Rheinland for the Commission of the European Communities, 1984.

Flanagan, Roger and George Norman *Life Cycle Costing for Construction* London, Surveyor Publications for The Royal Institution of Chartered Surveyors, c. 1983.

Frampton, Kenneth. *Modern Architecture: a Critical History.* London, Thames and Hudson, 1985.

Friedemann & Johnson Consultants GmbH. *Retrofitting of Metering and Control Technology for Heating Systems in Residential Buildings.* Berlin, Friedemann & Johnson - OPET for the European Commission, 1994.

Information Action: Photovoltaics in Buildings. Leaflet describing an ALTENER sponsored project involving IT Power Ltd., Ove Arup & Partners, Newcastle Photovoltaics Applications Centre, University of Northumbria, and BP Solar Ltd.

Jones Lang Wooton, McKenna & Co, and Gardiner & Theobald. *A New Balance: Buildings and the Environment: a Guide for Property Owners and Developers.* London, 1991.

Littlefair, P. J. *Site Layout Planning for Daylight and Sunlight.* (BR 209). Watford, Building Research Establishment, 1991

Netherlands. Ministry of Housing, Physical Planning and the Environment. Environmental Inspectorate for Government Buildings. *Easter Letter, 1995.* Amhem, RGD, 1995.

Nisson, J. D. Ned and Guatam Dutt. *The Superinsulated Home Book.* John Wiley & Sons, 1985.

Rattenbury, Kester. "Houseplants can beat sick building syndrome" *in Building Design ,* 9 November, 1990.

Slater, A.I. and P.J. Davidson. *Energy Efficient Lighting in Buildings.* Garston, BRECSU - OPET for the Commission of the European Communities, 1991.

Treble, Frederick C. *Solar Electricity: a Layman's Guide to the Generation of Electricity by the Direct Conversion of Solar Energy.* Birmingham, Solar Energy Society, 1993.

Tucker, Selwyn N. and Graham J. Treolar. "Energy embodied in construction and refurbishment of buildings." *in Buildings and their Environment: Proceedings of the First International Conference, Building Research Establishment, Watford, UK, 16-20 May, 1994.*

Vaughan, Nigel and Phil Jones. "Making the most of passive solar design". *In Building Services,* vol. 16, no. 11, November 1994. pp. 39-41.

Warmer Campaign. *Waste Recycling.* (Warmer Factsheet) Tunbridge Wells, The Warmer Campaign, 1990.

Wood, Ronald A. and Margaret D. Burchett. "The role of interior landscaping in the health and well being of building occupants." in *Healthy Buildings '95 : an International Conference on Healthy Buildings in Mild Climate, Milan, September 1995.* Proceedings, Volume I.

World Resource Foundation. *Construction and Demolition Wastes.* (Information Sheet) Tonbridge, Kent, The World Resource Foundation, 1995.

INDEX